AMERICANS INTO ORBIT
The Story of Project Mercury

In the fall of 1958, dismayed by the American lag in the space race with the Soviet Union, the United States government handed a group of engineers and scientists a most challenging assignment. Their job was to send a manned space capsule into orbit around the earth, study the man's ability to live and work in space, and then return the man and the capsule safely back to earth. The program would be called Project Mercury.

With great clarity, Gene Gurney describes the complex activities of Project Mercury—the designing, constructing and testing of the space capsule, the establishing of the Cape Canaveral Control Center and tracking stations, the selection and training of the seven astronauts, and the exciting flights of the first courageous space pilots.

Bill —   Oct. 28, 1964

On the occasion of your
Coming-Out Party —

The Fortmillers

AMERICANS INTO ORBIT

The Story of Project Mercury

Gene Gurney

Illustrated with photographs Random House N. Y.

PHOTOGRAPH CREDITS. The pictures used in this book are from the National Aeronautics and Space Administration, with the following exceptions: Bettmann Archive—page 35; British Information Service—page 29 (left); Esther C. Goddard—page 37 (right); Sovfoto—page 136; United Press—page 166; U. S. Air Force—page 29 (right); U. S. Army—pages 45, 53; U. S. Navy—page 51 (left); Wide World—pages 41, 51 (right), 59, 65 (top), 69 (bottom), 77, 143 (bottom), 147 (bottom), 149, 155 (top), 161 (top), 171

5 1263

CONTENTS

1. Project Mercury Sends a Man Into Space   3
2. Why Do We Explore Space?   24
3. Space Exploration Begins   33
4. Project Mercury   49
5. The Equipment for Exploring Space   63
6. Choosing the Mercury Astronaut   75
7. The Mercury Astronauts   85
8. The Mercury Astronauts Get Ready
   to Explore Space   96
9. Test Shots for Project Mercury   109
10. Other United States Space Projects   121
11. The Soviet Union's Space Program   132
12. Countdown   141
13. Three Times around the Earth   152
14. After Project Mercury   168
    Selected List ot Satellites and Probes   177
    Glossary   179
    Index   185

AMERICANS INTO ORBIT
The Story of Project Mercury

I. PROJECT MERCURY SENDS A MAN INTO SPACE

Cape Canaveral is a wedge-shaped strip of sand jutting out into the Atlantic from Florida's east coast. At one time it was almost unknown, except to the few fishermen who lived there. But on the morning of May 5, 1961, it seemed that there could be no one in all of the United States who hadn't heard of Cape Canaveral. Everybody was talking about what was happening there. People listened to transistor radios as they walked along the street. They gathered in groups to discuss the latest news bulletins.

"There has been a delay down at the Cape," they said. Then: "They're counting again! Things are moving along now!"

What was happening at Cape Canaveral on that fine, spring morning?

No longer a lonely stretch of sandy beach, Cape Canaveral was now part of the Atlantic Missile Range— the place from which the United States hoped to send a man on a ride through space. After months of planning and preparation everything was at last ready for the momentous journey. Since long before dawn the Cape had been bright with lights as tense workers got ready to send the first American into space.

Who was he? Who was this brave man who was going to travel to a point more than 100 miles above the surface of the earth? His name was Alan B. Shepard, Jr., and he was one of the seven astronauts of Project Mercury.

Project Mercury was the name given to the United States' program for putting a space capsule with a man in it into orbit around the earth. During the flight, scientists would study man's ability to survive in space. Then, perhaps most important of all, the man and the capsule were to be returned safely to earth.

Before a capsule with a human passenger could be sent into orbit, it was first necessary to send one just part of the way to be sure that everything was working as it should. And that was what was happening at Cape Canaveral on the morning of May 5. A manned Mercury capsule was going to be shot more than 100 miles up into space, above the earth's atmosphere. Then it would come back down again.

It was an important test. If the flight was a success, Project Mercury would be well on the way to sending a man all the way around the earth. Failure would mean many months of work before the test could be tried again.

There was a special reason why the attention of the whole country was centered on Cape Canaveral. The Soviet Union had already sent a man into space. They

Aerial view showing the construction of guided missile launching pads at Cape Canaveral, Florida.

had done it three weeks earlier, on April 12. Their spaceship, named the *Vostok*, which means "East," had gone completely around the earth in 87 minutes. It had carried a young man named Yuri Gagarin, the world's first spaceman.

The Soviet Union's announcement had been a great shock to the American people, who had always considered themselves to be leaders in science. It meant that the Soviet Union had taken the lead in the important business of sending a man into space.

The first American space flight had been scheduled for Tuesday, May 2. The weather forecast had not been good, and the day proved to be too cloudy for cameras to record the flight properly. Two days passed before the next try.

On Friday the weather was better. Astronaut Alan Shepard's big day began shortly after one o'clock in the morning when he was awakened in his room in Cape Canaveral's Hangar S. Sharing the room with him was John Glenn, the astronaut who had been chosen to take Shepard's place in case Shepard was unable to make the trip. In all, there were seven astronauts in the Project Mercury program. Three of them had been chosen as possibilities for the first Mercury flight, and Shepard had been picked as the one to go. John Glenn was his alternate. The third astronaut, Virgil Grissom, was on hand to help.

Both Alan Shepard and John Glenn had been getting ready for the trip into space. Since Saturday they had been on a special low-residue diet. They had taken,

and passed, numerous physical checkups. Their home
had been Hangar S. Now they went to eat the special
breakfast that had been prepared for them — orange
juice, eggs, steak, and toast. America's first spaceman
was not going to be hungry during his trip.

There was one last physical examination for both
men. Shepard proved to be in excellent shape for the
flight. He would be the one to go.

The astronaut began the complicated process of getting dressed for a trip into space. First he put on long
underwear which was patched in several places with a
screenlike material through which air could circulate
freely. On his feet were white socks and a pair of can-
vas slippers. Then doctors attached instruments called
sensors to various places on his body. The sensors
would tell them how the astronaut reacted to his flight
through space. The scientists wanted to find out what
happened to his temperature. Would it go up or down?
Would his heart beat rapidly when he was hurtling
along at 5,180 miles an hour? Would he have trouble
breathing? This information was important to the future of America's space program.

The astronaut had to be helped into his space suit.
It was a one-piece suit, made of nylon and rubber,
which tied at his chest, legs, and arms. The outside
was coated with a silvery, aluminum-like substance that
would protect the astronaut from heat and radiation.

The Project Mercury pressure suit had been selected
after six months of testing three possible choices. The
suits were worn for as long as 24 hours at a time to

find out how comfortable they were. They were tried out in temperatures as high as 180 degrees. The one that was finally chosen was a modification of a pressurized flight suit that had been developed by the Navy. The National Aeronautics and Space Administration ordered 20 of them from the B. F. Goodrich Company. They cost about $4,000 each. The astronauts were supplied with two custom-fitted suits apiece.

Air flows into the suit at the waist and circulates through the underwear-like suit beneath it. The air is then exhausted through a pipe in the helmet and sent to an air-conditioning system located beneath the astronaut's couch. After purification it is recirculated through the pressure suit.

The suit would be inflated only if the cabin pressurization system failed. Then it would automatically supply the pressure needed to keep the astronaut alive in space. Under ordinary conditions the suit serves as an air-conditioning system in addition to the one built into the capsule. It helps keep the astronaut comfortable.

For Shepard's feet there were silver-colored boots. On his head he wore a helmet that looked very much like the kind football players wear, but it contained radio microphones and earphones and it had a plastic facepiece. The helmet was secured to a metal ring at the neck of the space suit. For his hands there were gloves which fastened to his sleeves.

After the pressurization of his suit had been checked, the astronaut was ready to go. Outside Hangar S a van was waiting to take him to his space capsule.

On the morning of the fateful day Astronaut Alan Shepard gets into his space suit in Hangar S.

At Pad 5, the launching site, missile crews and Project Mercury officials had been on the job for hours. There were a great many things to be done before a man could be sent into space.

It was shortly after five o'clock and still dark when Shepard left the van at Pad 5. There, high above him, was the capsule in which he would ride. Beneath it was the Redstone rocket that would boost it up into space. The Redstone rocket had been chosen for the first space flight because it was the most reliable of all America's rockets. Long and slender, its sides were covered with frost from the liquid oxygen that was escaping in great clouds. Liquid oxygen, or lox, in combination with ethyl alcohol, would provide the fuel for the rocket's engine.

The astronaut, in his silver suit, paused for one last look around him. Huge floodlights gave an almost unreal sharpness to the scene. The capsule, which had been named Freedom 7 by Shepard, was still covered by a green plastic work platform. An elevator would carry Shepard up the 60 feet to this "greenhouse."

As he got into the elevator, a cheer arose from the launching-pad crewmen. There were cries of "Good luck!" and "Have a good trip!" These men and hundreds more had worked hard to make this Project Mercury flight a success.

John Glenn was waiting on the platform outside Freedom 7. He had given the ten-by-six-foot capsule a thorough preflight check. Everything was ready to go.

Shepard talked briefly with Glenn and with Virgil

Shepard is helped onto the gantry elevator, which will take him up to his capsule.

Astronaut Shepard enters his space craft, Freedom 7, from which he communicates during countdown with flight controllers in the Cape Canaveral blockhouse.

Grissom, who had joined them on the platform. At 5:20 A.M. he climbed into the capsule. White-gowned technicians helped him through the narrow hatch.

Attached to the instrument panel, where no one but Alan Shepard could see it, John Glenn had left a note. It said, No HANDBALL PLAYING IN THIS AREA. This made the astronaut laugh, because there was barely room enough for one man inside the tiny cockpit. John Glenn laughed too and then removed his sign.

The skillful hands of the technicians fastened the straps that held Shepard to his contour couch, made the final connections into his pressure suit, and took care of the necessary last-minute adjustments.

Then Guenter Wendt, pad leader for the launching, reached in for a final handshake and a last "Good luck!" The hatch door was pushed into place and fastened. The time was 6:10.

Alan Shepard got busy at once. He had many things to do—check lists to run through, switches to test, instruments to watch. And he was in telephone contact with the blockhouse, where technicians and Project Mercury officials were keeping an electronic watch on the Redstone, the capsule, and the astronaut.

All this time the rocket and the capsule had been surrounded by a red-and-white service tower called a gantry. Shortly after 6:30, just as the sun was rising, the workers finished the things that had to be done outside the capsule. The gantry, which was on tracks, was rolled away. Now everyone could see the gray-black Mercury capsule, shaped something like a television tube, standing high in the air above the slender Redstone rocket. Above the capsule a bright-orange escape rocket on a 16-foot tripod caught the sun's first rays. If something went wrong immediately after the launching, the escape rocket would carry the capsule and its passenger safely away from the Redstone.

A countdown precedes every rocket launching at Cape Canaveral. In a countdown the letter "T" stands for take-off time. T minus 20 means that there are still 20 minutes to go. At T zero the rocket is fired. When something goes wrong and has to be fixed, the countdown stops. The delay is known as a hold.

The countdown for the Mercury launching had reached T minus 15 when clouds rolled in over the Cape. Scientists expected to learn a great deal from pictures taken of the launching and the first few seconds of the rocket's flight. So the count became "T minus 15 and holding," while a recheck was made on the weather.

Then it was discovered that an inverter, a device for changing direct current to alternating current, wasn't working properly. The gantry had to be rolled back into position around the rocket to enable technicians to locate the trouble.

Eighty-six minutes later the inverter was fixed, and the gantry was rolled away. The weather had improved, so the countdown was resumed.

Then there was another hold. By this time Astronaut Shepard had been in the capsule for almost four hours, lying strapped to his contour couch. But this latest hold was just a short one—to check a pressure gauge.

"T minus 2!"

Time for a last communication from the blockhouse. Time to set the temperature controls for the pressure suit and the capsule cabin. The periscope through which Shepard had been able to watch what was happening on the ground was retracted into the capsule.

The count was in seconds now: "10, 9, 8, 7, 6, 5, 4, 3, 2, 1, zero!"

"Ignition . . . Mainstage . . . Lift-off!"

From the capsule came the answer, "Roger, lift-off, and the clock is started."

Exactly at lift-off the astronaut had started a stop watch. With a roar the Redstone was on its way, lifting Freedom 7 and its passenger up, up, up.

Within the capsule America's first spaceman had braced himself for the rapid climb into space. His instruments told him what was happening. Through his headphones he could hear the Capsule Communicator who was monitoring his flight at the Mercury Control Center. From his capsule he could transmit messages to the Control Center to let them know how things were going.

The first minute of flight, as the rocket started its climb, was smooth—smoother than the astronaut had expected. Then the capsule began to vibrate as it reached supersonic speed and passed through the zone where its speed met the greatest resistance from the air. This didn't last long, however.

Soon Shepard was able to report: "O.K. It's a lot smoother now. A lot smoother."

Two minutes after take-off the Redstone rocket had

carried the Mercury capsule to a height of 25 miles. Shepard could feel the acceleration pushing him back into his couch. His heart was pumping hard, and all the air seemed to have been squeezed out of his lungs.

Right on schedule, after a little more than two minutes of flight, the Redstone's engine burned out. Now Shepard could feel his forward speed decrease.

But things began to happen fast. With a roaring noise, the escape tower, no longer needed, blew off. Then it was time for the capsule to leave the burned-out rocket. This was the most critical moment of the flight. If the rocket and the capsule didn't separate, Shepard would try to bail out. In all probability rocket, capsule, and astronaut would fall back into the ocean.

However, the explosive bolts in the clamp holding the capsule to the rocket fired as they were supposed to. The clamp fell away, and three small rockets in the capsule lifted it away from the spent Redstone.

With relief the astronaut heard the three rockets go off. When he saw the green light on his instrument panel, he reported: "Cap. sep. is green."

The capsule had now reached a point where the force of its motion away from the earth was exactly equal to the force of gravity pulling it toward the earth. Freedom 7 and its passenger were both weightless. Shepard was strapped to his couch, but he could feel the absence of all pressure. He reported it pleasant and relaxing. He was able to breathe, move, and talk without difficulty. He observed that the ends of his straps seemed to be floating in the air.

The slender gray-black Mercury-Redstone III soars into the air, carrying the first American into space.

The capsule had been in a slow 180-degree turn which placed its blunt end forward. That end contained a heat-dispersing shield to protect the capsule from the great heat it would encounter on reëntering the earth's atmosphere. The turn-about was completed, and the periscope had come back out. The busy astronaut had no time to look at the view. He was about to fly the capsule himself.

So far, Freedom 7 had been on automatic pilot, flying a controlled, pre-set course. Now Shepard took over. He raised and lowered the blunt end, turned the capsule from side to side, and finally took over control of the roll motion. He was flying his space ship!

Then he looked out through the periscope. He was a hundred miles above the earth. "What a beautiful view!" he exclaimed.

He could see northward as far as the Carolina coast, all the way west across Florida to Tampa Bay. To the south he could make out some of the islands in the Bahamas. The ocean was a deep, deep blue shading off to light green where the water was shallow. The sky was deep blue, too, almost black, because at that height there were no dust particles to reflect light.

All this time Freedom 7 had been climbing. The Redstone rocket could not lift the capsule high enough to send it into orbit. It was making a suborbital, or ballistic, flight, following a high, curving arc. When its forward motion was spent it would fall back to earth. A space ship actually in orbit, however, would continue on its path around the earth for a long time. It would be traveling so high and so fast that its forward motion would counteract the force of gravity pulling it toward the earth. To get such a spaceship out of orbit, it would first be necessary to slow down the capsule. The slowing down would also reduce the force with which the spaceship hit the earth's atmosphere as it came down.

This first attempt was a practice flight for that first trip into orbit around the earth. Although Freedom 7 could get down without it, Astronaut Shepard got ready for the firing of three braking rockets attached to the capsule's blunt end. They were called retro-rockets and would be needed when Project Mercury sent a man into orbit. He raised the blunt end of the capsule. The rockets fired in sequence.

"Retro 1 fired, very smooth," he reported.

Then: "Retro 2. Retro 3. All three retros are fired."

Freedom 7, which had reached a height of 116.5 miles above the earth, slowed and then started down.

The used rockets were supposed to be jettisoned automatically. Through his periscope Shepard could see the straps that held the rockets fall. But his instrument panel did not show the green light that meant the rockets were safely out of the way.

He told the Control Center: "I do not have a light. I see the straps falling away. I heard a noise. I will use override."

He then pushed the override button, which had been installed to take care of just such a failure in the automatic system.

His next transmission to the Control Center was: "Override used. The light is green."

Shepard had now pointed his capsule down at a 40-degree angle. Once again the capsule encountered increasing resistance. As Freedom 7 penetrated the earth's atmosphere, the 160-pound Shepard was feeling a pressure of 1,760 pounds. He managed to grunt out, "O.K., O.K., O.K.," to tell the men at the Control Center that the pressure wasn't too much for him.

The temperature in the capsule remained a comfortable 85 degrees as the spaceship rushed through the rapidly thickening atmosphere.

So far everything had gone without a hitch. But the astronaut still had ahead of him a landing in the ocean. The Mercury Control Center had been keeping a careful watch on the capsule's flight. The scientists there could tell that Freedom 7 was going to land just where they expected. "Your impact will be right on the button," they told the astronaut.

That was good news, for it meant that he would land where ships and planes were waiting to snatch him quickly from the water.

When the descending capsule reached 21,000 feet, a small parachute called a drogue was released from its narrow end. It helped to slow the capsule and keep it steady. At 10,000 feet the main parachute, a huge orange-and-white canopy, came out. It would lower the capsule into the water as gently as possible.

To get ready for the water landing, Shepard opened the face plate of his helmet and removed some of the

A Marine helicopter hooks onto Freedom 7 and Astronaut Shepard, in body harness, is pulled to safety.

straps that had been holding him to his couch. Through a porthole he could see the water racing up to meet him. He was getting close. He braced himself and—*smack!*—he had landed.

The capsule went down into the water and over on its side. Then it slowly righted itself. As soon as his radio antenna was out of the water, Shepard sent the message that the whole country was waiting to hear: ". . . everything A-O.K."

A Marine helicopter had been hovering near the spot where the capsule landed. Its pilot called Shepard on the radio to say the helicopter was above the capsule and ready to hook on. There was a thud as the hook caught the top of the capsule.

"O.K.," the pilot called, "you've got two minutes to come out."

Water was still washing over the porthole and Shepard didn't want a wave to come bursting through the hatch when he opened it.

"Can you bring me up a bit?" he asked.

The capsule rose in the water.

"I'll be out in thirty seconds."

Shepard removed his helmet and took a last look around Freedom 7. It was a good capsule and had done its job well. He opened the hatch, pulled himself through, and slipped into the sling which the helicopter had lowered for him. He rode in the sling up to the helicopter, which then took him to the *Lake Champlain,* the flagship of the Space Capsule Recovery Task Force.

The helicopter also carried the Freedom 7 to the *Lake Champlain*.

America's first voyage into space was over. Her first spaceman had reached a height of 116.5 miles. He had landed safely in the ocean 302 miles from Cape Canaveral. His trip to space and back had taken just 15 minutes.

II. WHY DO WE EXPLORE SPACE?

Space begins at the outside edges of the earth's atmosphere and extends on and on endlessly. There is no exact place where space starts because the earth's atmosphere gets thinner gradually. Space could be said to begin where there is not enough oxygen to keep a man alive, or where there is no longer enough atmosphere to support an airplane. Or it could begin where there is not a trace of the earth's atmosphere left. For purposes of exploration, many scientists think of space as beginning about 20 miles above the earth's surface. Only one per cent of the earth's atmosphere is above this point and it is very thin indeed.

Space is vast, but it is not empty. It contains meteors, cosmic rays, and various forms of electromagnetic radiation. It contains the solar system of which the earth is a part—nine planets revolving around the sun. There are thousands of smaller bodies moving within this solar system.

Our sun is only one star in a vast galaxy of 200 billion stars. And there are billions of galaxies in the dis-

tant reaches of space. It is no wonder that the possibility of exploring space has intrigued men for hundreds of years.

From the beginning of history, men have been studying the stars. The Hebrews, the Egyptians, the Greeks, and other ancient peoples left behind written accounts of what they thought the universe was like. But they, and those that lived hundreds of years later, could learn no more about the stars than what they could see by gazing upward on a clear night.

All this was changed when the telescope was invented. This wonderful device which uses lenses to form enlarged images of distant objects came to us from Holland. According to one story the children of a Dutch spectacle-maker were playing in his shop one day. On his workbench were several lenses all polished and ready to be put into frames for spectacles. One of the children picked up two of the lenses and looked through them both at once. He looked at the clock on a church tower down the street. To his surprise the clock was magnified; he could see it easily. His father looked through the two lenses and realized that it was an important discovery. In the year 1608 the Dutch government gave the spectacle-maker, whose name was Hans Lippershey, 900 florins for his invention of the telescope.

News of the telescope spread rapidly throughout Europe. In Italy an astronomer and physicist named Galileo heard about it. He was a very clever man and soon had made a telescope of his own. In 1609 he looked at the sky through a telescope for the first time. He saw things that had never been seen before. He discovered that the Milky Way was made up of stars. He saw the moons of the planet Jupiter, the spots on the sun, and the mountainous surface of the moon.

Since Galileo's day telescopes have become much more powerful, and we can see farther and better with them. With cameras we can take pictures to study later. And now we have radio telescopes to help us learn about the radiations coming from objects in space.

As wonderful as these telescopes are, they can tell us about space only as it is seen through the earth's atmosphere, which we know distorts and obscures much that we want to see. In order to observe more clearly, scientists have been using rockets to send sensitive equipment high above the earth where there is little or no dust and vapor. The scientific instruments carried aloft in these space probes have provided a great amount of important new data. But scientists still want to know much more about space. And the things they want to know can best be learned if a man is sent up there to collect the information, analyze the findings, and describe what he has observed.

To send a man into space is much more difficult than to send up a collection of instruments. Man is constructed to live in the earth's atmosphere, not in space where there is no air for him to breathe, no food for him to eat, no gravity to give him stability. The extreme temperatures in space can either roast or freeze him to death. For man, space is a dark, soundless, hostile environment. It contains harmful forms of radiation from which he must be protected. And he must be protected from the meteors and the many smaller particles that abound in space.

Obviously, for his space traveling, man needs some sort of a protective capsule which will shield him and provide an environment in which he can live. And the capsule must be strong enough to withstand the tremendous speed and pressure needed to lift it and its human passenger up through the earth's atmosphere and into space. The rockets we have today—and those we will have in the foreseeable future—must travel very fast in order to get out of the earth's atmosphere before their fuel is used up. The trip from the launching pad up into space is more than a man can survive unless he is well protected from the effects of the rapid upward movement.

In space the capsule will have to supply him with all the necessities of life. Oxygen and pressurization are two vital requirements. At sea level the pressure of the air is almost 15 pounds per square inch. Approximately 21 per cent of it is oxygen, 78 per cent is nitrogen, and the rest is made up of argon and other gases. A man will do his work best and be most comfortable if these conditions are duplicated inside his sealed space capsule. He will need to be supplied with two pounds of oxygen a day. This oxygen could be carried from the earth in tanks; it could be produced in the capsule. Or used oxygen could be recovered and then used over and over again.

Left. *The giant reflector bowl of the Jodrell Bank radio telescope in England is 250 feet in diameter and weighs 750 tons. Right. Dr. James A. Van Allen examines the special equipment to be included in Pioneer IV for radiation detection.*

Equally important, the carbon dioxide, which is exhaled at about the same rate that oxygen is inhaled, must be removed from the capsule along with other waste materials.

Another problem is that of temperature. The side of the space capsule facing the sun will become unbearably hot from absorbing the sun's rays. But the side away from the sun will remain ice cold. If the spaceman is to be kept alive, his capsule must have an efficient air-conditioning system.

The traveler in space will also need to carry his food with him. If he is going to be in space for more than a short time, he will have to eat things that keep well and have little bulk. The problem of food supply will be complicated by the fact that both the spaceman and what he eats will be weightless once they are beyond the gravitational pull of the earth. Much of his food will be in liquid form and he will eat it from tubes or bottles.

Weightlessness is something we don't know very much about. We have discovered that for some people it is a pleasant experience. Others become ill with something like seasickness. During periods of weightlessness, up and down become confused and movements are difficult to control. Until a spaceman has experienced a really long period of weightlessness in flight, we can only guess at how much of a problem it will be. The first American astronaut to go into orbit, Lieutenant Colonel John Glenn, reported that weightlessness in flight was a pleasant feeling for him.

Another potential problem for the space traveler is loneliness and a feeling of being isolated from the earth. Some scientists think that he may become "space happy" in a very short period of time. The effects of isolation have been studied by placing volunteers in rooms resembling the interior of a spaceship. In some cases the tests have been made in complete darkness. But the people being tested know they are safely on earth and not hurtling through space, so we still don't know for sure what will happen. The first long space trip will tell us a great deal about this problem too.

Problems will exist outside as well as inside the space capsule. Ultraviolet rays, x-rays, and other forms of radiation abound in space, and protection from them must be provided. Radiation seems to be concentrated in two zones roughly 2,300 miles and 11,000 miles from the earth's surface. They are separated by a region called the "slot," where radiation is at a minimum. The two radiation zones are called the Van Allen belts in honor of the physicist, Dr. James A. Van Allen. He was responsible for the instruments which, when sent aloft in January, 1958, first detected the two regions of intense radiation.

Even if the spaceship were heavily shielded from the harmful effects of radiation, it would have no protection from collision with a meteor. Some scientists feel that there aren't enough large meteors in space for this to be a problem, but just one collision with a meteor would demolish a space craft. And space is full of small particles called micrometeors. Continuous bombardment by micrometeors will eventually cause enough damage to hinder the operation of the spaceship.

Man's further exploration of space is certainly not going to be easy. The important question is: Will his increased knowledge be worth the considerable effort required to obtain it? Scientists say that the answer is yes. The knowledge that we gain about space can be used to greatly benefit mankind.

Weather forecasting has already become more accurate through the use of weather satellites traveling around the earth. Communication satellites will make world-wide television possible, and they will be able to relay our ever growing number of transoceanic messages. Other satellites will make navigation easier for ships and planes. Also, from space we will get a better picture of the shape and structure of the earth. In this way we will be able to make our maps more accurate.

These things can all be done by satellites without a human crew. Their operations can be controlled from the earth. But there is a limit to what can be done without a man on the spot, using his ability to observe, to reason, and to cope with the unexpected. Manned space laboratories will be able to carry out a wide range of investigation in many fields.

The important long-term benefits of space exploration lie in increased knowledge of our universe. Man has always been an explorer of the unknown, and space is one of the few areas still waiting to be explored. The unraveling of its mysteries may produce changes greater than anything mankind has yet known.

III. SPACE EXPLORATION BEGINS

For many years we could do no more than study space with our telescopes, because there was no way to get up beyond the atmosphere. The modern rocket has changed all that. Rockets can be made powerful enough to hurl objects hundreds of miles away from the earth.

The rocket is not a new thing—the Chinese were using them as early as A.D. 1232. The Chinese already knew about gunpowder. And they discovered that, when a tube of gunpowder was fastened to the shaft of an arrow and ignited, the arrow would dart out, spreading fire as it went. Although they did not realize it, the Chinese had discovered the principle of rocket propulsion. The gases expelled by the burning gunpowder sent the arrow to its target.

In the seventeenth century Sir Isaac Newton, an English mathematician, became interested in the study of motion. He worked out three laws, or rules, that explained why things moved. The first of Newton's laws of motion states that a body remains at rest or in motion unless it is acted upon by some outside force. The second law states that the force acting upon this body will cause it to move in the direction of the force. And the third law says that to every action there is an equal and opposite reaction.

It is Newton's third law that explains what makes a rocket shoot up into space. As fuel burns within the rocket, gases are produced which push against the rocket. The rocket, in turn, pushes the gases backward. In doing so, it moves forward.

Just as the Chinese were the first to develop rockets, they were the first to try to use them for flight. About the year A.D. 1500, a Chinese adventurer named Wan-Hoo fastened a chair between two kites. Behind the chair he attached 47 gunpowder rockets. Wan-Hoo climbed into his chair, his servants lit the rockets, and —*whoosh!*—he was gone. No trace of Wan-Hoo or his rocket chair was ever found.

In spite of Wan-Hoo's pioneering effort to use rockets for flight, or perhaps because of it, the rocket continued to be used as a military weapon almost exclusively. During the War of 1812 the British used powerful rockets to attack Fort McHenry near Baltimore, Maryland. Among those who saw the rockets fall on Fort McHenry was Francis Scott Key. When he wrote our national anthem he mentioned "the rocket's red glare."

By the end of the nineteenth century, however, there were several proposed plans for building rocket ships. And in 1903 a Russian schoolteacher named Konstantin Ziolkovsky wrote a very good description of space travel with rockets. His studies had convinced him that with

*During the War of 1812 British rockets bombarded Fort Mc-
Henry near Baltimore.*

liquid-fuel rockets it would be possible to travel beyond the atmosphere. Ziolkovsky wrote papers in which he described the results of his study and experiments. He sent these articles to scientific societies. Unfortunately his work received little attention. It was not until after World War I that a growing interest in rocketry brought him recognition and some help from the Russian government.

By the time Konstantin Ziolkovsky died in 1935, he had become a national hero. His writings have been reprinted, and a crater on the moon has been named for him. The Soviet government refers to Ziolkovsky as the "Father of Space Travel."

America's first rocket expert was a physics professor named Robert H. Goddard. He was born in 1882 and grew up in Boston, Massachusetts. Like Konstantin Ziolkovsky, Robert Goddard became interested in the use of liquid-fuel rockets for space travel. He too was convinced that space travel was possible. Unlike Ziolkovsky, Goddard was able to transform his theories about rockets into reality. On March 16, 1926, from a snow-covered field in Auburn, Massachusetts, he successfully fired the world's first liquid-fueled rocket. It shot up to a height of 184 feet in 2½ seconds. Goddard went on to develop a pump capable of supplying the liquid fuel at a rapid rate and a gyroscope device to guide rockets in flight. He continued to improve his rockets until in 1935 he was able to send one to a height of 7,500 feet.

Before that experiment, however, neighbors' complaints about the noise of Dr. Goddard's rockets had

Left. *Robert Goddard beside his first successful liquid-fuel rocket.* Right. *A Goddard rocket in flight near Roswell, New Mexico, in 1937.*

forced him to move to the southwestern part of the United States. At Roswell, New Mexico, where there were few people to be bothered and ideal conditions for testing, he carried on his rocket experiments until his death in 1945.

In the years before World War II, Dr. Goddard's work was almost unnoticed. Very few people in the United States were interested in rockets. Rockets were just something to read about in science-fiction stories. But in far-off Silesia a young German named Wernher von Braun heard about Dr. Goddard and his work with rockets. Wernher wanted to become a rocket scientist too, and he read everything he could find about rockets. Rocketry was a popular subject in Germany. Newspapers and magazines carried stories about high-altitude rockets, rocket cars, and trips to the moon.

One day Wernher met Hermann Oberth, the most famous of the German rocket scientists. Soon he was working with Oberth on rocket experiments in his spare time. He joined the German rocket society called *Verein für Raumschiffahrt* (which in English means Society for Space Travel). The members of the society conducted rocket experiments at a field near Berlin.

By 1932 Germany was seriously considering the development of the rocket for use as a powerful weapon. The army offered to send young von Braun to the University of Berlin to study physics. In addition he would be allowed to use army facilities for rocket experiments. Von Braun accepted the offer, and for two years he was a student at the university. When he received his degree he was immediately given the job of developing a military rocket. What the army wanted was a really big rocket, one that could travel 160 miles at a top speed of 3,350 miles an hour. It was to carry one ton of explosives in its nose. To build it, the leading German rocket experts were gathered together and put to work at a place called Peenemuende on the Baltic sea coast.

Wernher von Braun played a leading part in developing this rocket, which came to be known as the V-2. It was fired for the first time in October, 1942, three years after the outbreak of World War II. The test shot was a success, and the Germans began to build the sites from which they planned to launch their powerful rocket against Great Britain.

All did not go smoothly, however. British bombers dropped tons of bombs on Peenemuende. And von Braun was arrested by the Gestapo and charged with treason. He was released when it became apparent that V-2 production could not proceed without him, but precious time had been lost.

The first V-2s were fired against the British on September 8, 1944. Unlike the earlier V-1 "flying bomb," which was an aerial torpedo with wings and very noisy, the V-2 descended on its target without a sound. The slightly more than 1,000 V-2s that fell on Great Britain killed 2,855 people and seriously injured 6,268 more. In addition there was considerable damage to buildings. If the V-2 had been ready earlier, it might have altered the course of the war. But it came too late. By January, 1945, the Russian army was so close to Peenemuende that the rocket experts were forced to flee. They decided to go to where they could surrender to the Americans. With some difficulty they made their way to Reutte, Austria, in the Bavarian Alps. There they waited until the Americans were near.

Because Wernher's brother, Magnus, spoke the best English, he was sent to find some American soldiers to surrender to. When he found them he said, "We are a group of rocket specialists up in the mountains. We want to see your commander and surrender to the Americans."

It so happened that plans had already been made for questioning the Peenemuende rocket specialists if they could be found. The project was known as "Operation Paperclip," because the cards of the most important men were marked with paper clips. There was much excitement when it was learned that many of the rocket experts had been located. Because they knew so much about rockets, a number of them were brought to the United States for questioning. A Rocket Research and Development Center was established at El Paso, Texas. And under the leadership of Wernher von Braun, the German experts went to work. They began with the assembling and launching of V-2 rockets which had been captured in Germany. These rockets carried no high explosives. Instead they were equipped with scientific instruments.

Wernher von Braun (center) and two other German scientists check a V-2 engine being readied for a test at White Sands, New Mexico, in 1946.

The United States had already begun its exploration of space with "sounding rockets." A sounding rocket is one that travels not more than 3,950 miles before falling back to the earth's surface. It carries instruments which examine the area through which the rocket is traveling. In the beginning, of course, the rockets didn't go nearly so high as 3,950 miles. One of the first American sounding rockets reached a height of 43½ miles. It was a WAC Corporal launched in 1945 from the newly established rocket-testing center at White Sands, New Mexico.

By the next year the V-2s brought from Germany had been assembled and were ready for firing. Carrying delicate scientific instruments instead of deadly explosives, they gathered information from altitudes high above the earth's surface. This information enabled scientists to check on things they had only guessed at before. One of the V-2s reached a height of 137 miles. But since the V-2 had been designed to demolish a target with a ton of high explosives, it wasn't too well suited to high-altitude research. It was eventually modified and given the name Viking.

The WAC Corporal had been too small to travel very high. It too was improved. In February, 1949, at White Sands, a WAC Corporal was mounted on a modified V-2 rocket. The V-2 carried the WAC Corporal to a height of 20 miles. Then the two rockets separated and the WAC Corporal was fired. It climbed to a record-breaking height of 250 miles, carrying 50 pounds of radio and electronic equipment. This was a very important rocket firing because it proved that a two-stage rocket was possible. By building rockets with two or more stages, or units, scientists could send them much higher than one rocket could travel alone.

These were exciting days for the workers at the White Sands Proving Ground. They were constantly learning new things about rocket design and performance. The instruments sent aloft revealed amazing facts. Scientists all over the country sent in suggestions for improving the instruments, as well as ideas for new data to be collected. There were so many things to be studied that it was difficult to decide which ones to work on first.

Once the scientists had determined which data were to be gathered by a new rocket, they had to select the instruments that would best do the job. Then these instruments had to be fitted into the small nose cone of the rocket. When a single rocket was being used to measure more than one thing, the instruments had to be placed where they would not interfere with one another. A great deal of ingenuity went into the designing of the instruments that were carried by the White Sands rockets. They had to do their work in a very small space, and they had to be as foolproof as possible so that the information they gathered would be accurate.

Of course the data collected by a sounding rocket is useful only if it can be returned to the earth. Sometimes an automatic radio transmitter sends the information to a receiver on the ground. Such a transmitter is called a telemeter. Another method is to record the data, as it is collected, on film or magnetic tape carried in the rocket. If this is done, the rocket must be recovered when it returns to earth. In the early days of sounding rockets, many hours were spent searching the desert around the White Sands Proving Ground to find rockets that had managed to elude the scientists who were tracking them. Gradually, improved methods of tracking were developed until it was possible to send living animals up in rockets and recover them unharmed when they came down.

The sounding rockets themselves were improved, too. They went higher and carried more instruments. But they were still able to record high-altitude data for only a few minutes before falling back to earth. The next step was to send a space vehicle into orbit around the earth so that it could send back continuous information on conditions in space. Such a vehicle is called an artificial earth satellite. It is launched into orbit around the earth by sending it up at a very high speed. Its speed tends to carry the satellite away from the earth; at the same time gravity keeps pulling it toward the earth. At the point where these two forces are exactly balanced, the satellite will go into orbit around the earth.

Scientists are able to figure just how fast a satellite must be traveling to go into orbit. For example, if a satellite is to be sent around the earth at a height of 200 miles, it must reach a speed of 18,000 miles an hour. On the basis of the satellite's speed, scientists can also predict whether the path it will follow will be a truly

Three Army Ordnance technicians hold a WAC Corporal rocket in a vertical position.

circular one or one that resembles a closed curve. This last type is known as an elliptical orbit and is the one followed by most satellites.

Satellites can be built in a variety of shapes and sizes. The size, shape, and amount of the equipment to be carried into space play a big part in determining what a satellite will look like. The satellite is carried aloft at the forward end of a rocket which fires in stages, each stage falling away as its fuel is used up. The last stage must carry the satellite fast enough and far enough for it to go into orbit.

Rocket experts were able to launch an earth satellite on paper long before the first one was actually sent into space. They knew how fast it would have to travel, the path it would take, and even how long it would stay in orbit.

What they were waiting for was a rocket with sufficient power to lift the satellite high enough and fast enough. They also had to work out ways of stabilizing the motion of the satellite and guiding it in flight.

The scientists of the Soviet Union were the first to solve these problems. On October 4, 1957, the Soviet Union announced that it had successfully launched the first man-made satellite. Its speed of five miles a second was carrying it around the earth once every ninety-two minutes. As it whizzed along, it transmitted a "beep-beep" signal to the world below. *Sputnik,* or "Fellow-Traveler," as the Russians called their satellite, weighed 184 pounds. It measured 23 inches in diameter, about the size of a basketball.

The launching of Sputnik I marked the true beginning of the space age, and the Soviet Union was justly proud of what it had accomplished. At the end of World War II some of the German rocket scientists had also been captured by Russian soldiers. These men went to work for the Soviet Union just as Wernher von Braun and his colleagues had gone to work for the United States. During the years that Americans were experimenting with rockets at the White Sands Proving Ground, similar experiments were going on in the Soviet Union. Sometime during those years, the scientists there learned the secret of building rockets with tremendous boosting power.

That they had done so was demonstrated on November 3, 1957, when Sputnik II was sent into orbit. It weighed 1,120 pounds. And it carried a passenger! Along with instruments for measuring cosmic rays and solar radiation, and radio transmitters to report the data to earth, rode a dog named Laika. Her reactions to her ride through space were also radioed to earth.

Since 1957 a number of satellites have been placed in orbit around the earth. Some have even been sent into orbit around the sun. While these satellites have not created quite as much excitement as the first two Sputniks, each has helped turn into reality man's dream of escaping the forces that hold him to the earth.

Explorer I, which the United States orbited in 1958, gave us our first information on the Van Allen radiation belts. A third Sputnik, also launched in 1958, measured a variety of things including cosmic rays, magnetic fields, and radiation. It also reported on meteors in space. The fourth satellite in the United States Explorer series carried out a more detailed study of radiation belts. Other satellites have sent back information on weather. They have provided a better picture of what the earth really looks like and they have carried animals, enabling us to study the effect of space travel on living things.

These unmanned satellites added greatly to our knowledge of space, but they marked just the beginning of space exploration.

IV. PROJECT MERCURY

The beep-beep of that first Sputnik, as it traveled on its orbit around the earth in the fall of 1957, caused the United States to take a new look at its own space program. Our sounding rockets had supplied us with a great deal of valuable information about space, but how close were we to putting a satellite into orbit? We had been thinking about it for years, of course. In fact we had begun thinking about it long before the necessary equipment was available.

By the summer of 1954 Wernher von Braun felt that we had at last developed rockets that could do the job. He told a group of Army and Navy officials that the Redstone missile, combined with three smaller Loki rockets, which had also been developed by the Army's Redstone Arsenal, could boost a small satellite into orbit. This was good news indeed. The Army and the Navy decided to coöperate on the project, which was called Orbiter.

Then in the summer of 1955 the United States government announced an entirely different project. It was

Project Vanguard, a satellite program to be conducted in connection with the International Geophysical Year planned for 1957. Plans for Project Vanguard called for the use of no military equipment such as the Army's Redstone missile. Work began at once on the development of an entirely new rocket. Wernher von Braun's Project Orbiter was dropped.

Project Vanguard progress was slow, however. For one thing rocket development is expensive. The $22,-000,000 that had been set aside for the project turned out to be not nearly enough, and more money was hard to get. In the mid-1950s Americans were not yet convinced of the importance of developing rockets and satellites.

In December, 1956, the first stage of the Vanguard rocket was ready for its first test. Slim and glistening, it shot out over the Atlantic at 4,000 miles an hour. That test was a complete success, but there was still much work to be done. And as time went on, problems began to appear. The Vanguard satellite shot had been scheduled for the summer of 1957; then it was postponed to late fall.

In the meantime the Russians had put the first two Sputniks into orbit. And all the world was watching to see if the United States, too, could send a satellite into orbit. Unfortunately the very next Vanguard test shot on December 6, 1957, was a dismal failure. The rocket rose a few feet and then fell back on its launching pad in flames.

Left. *The Vanguard rocket tested in December, 1957, rose only a few feet, then fell back on the launching pad in flames.* Right. *On January 31, 1958, a Jupiter-C rocket put Explorer I, America's first artificial satellite, into orbit.*

Of course it was only a test shot, and our scientists had stressed that fact. The complex second stage of the rocket had never been fired before, and a perfect shot was unlikely. But the once beautiful rocket, burning on its launching pad, dealt a severe blow to American pride.

Meanwhile, what had happened to Project Orbiter, the first plan for putting up an American satellite? It had been shelved in favor of Project Vanguard, but it hadn't been forgotten. When the first Sputnik went up, Wernher von Braun told Neil McElroy, the man who was to be the new secretary of defense: "We can fire a satellite into orbit 60 days from the moment you give us a green light!"

And he did it! On January 31, 1958, the first American satellite was sent into orbit around the earth. Von Braun used a Jupiter-C rocket, an improved version of the Redstone rocket he had planned to use in 1954. The satellite, called Explorer I, weighed only 18 pounds, much less than the Sputniks, but it was up there. And Americans had been thoroughly awakened to the importance of space exploration.

On March 17, 1958, after more disheartening failures, a six-inch Vanguard satellite was finally sent into orbit. Nine days later von Braun and his rocket experts orbited a second Explorer; in July they sent up another. And in December, a few days before Christmas, one of the Atlas intercontinental ballistic missiles developed by the Air Force was placed in orbit. This shot was called Proj-

The face of Wernher von Braun (center) reflects the tension in the blockhouse as the moment approaches to launch Explorer III into orbit.

ect SCORE, the letters standing for Signal Communication by Orbiting Relay Equipment. The two-way communications system carried by the satellite enabled it to record the human voice in outer space and then send it back to earth. One of the recorded voices was that of President Eisenhower. His Christmas message was sent up to the satellite, which taped and stored it. At a signal from the ground the satellite rebroadcast the message to the world. It said:

"This is the President of the United States speaking.

"Through the marvels of scientific advance, my voice is coming to you from a satellite traveling in outer space.

"My message is a simple one.

"Through this unique means I convey to you and to all mankind America's wish for peace on earth and good will toward men everywhere."

The accelerated schedule of satellite launchings set in motion in 1958 was part of a revised United States space program. It had been revised because the Soviet Union's Sputniks had made us realize that we had been dragging our feet in space research.

Such progress as we had made had come from a number of projects often conducted quite independently of one another. The Army had developed and tested rockets at its White Sands Proving Ground. Later it set up a Guided Missile Development Division at Huntsville, Alabama, under the direction of Wernher von Braun. Explorer I had come from Huntsville.

The Air Force was also interested in guided missiles.

It opened a testing site at Cape Canaveral, Florida, and began work on a variety of missiles, one of which was the Atlas that broadcast President Eisenhower's message. Another Air Force project was the development of supersonic, high-altitude aircraft.

The Navy was experimenting with various types of missiles, and it was responsible for Project Vanguard.

In addition to these military agencies, there was a civilian organization engaged in space research. It was the National Advisory Committee for Aeronautics which, since 1915, had been dealing with problems of flight. As planes flew higher and faster, it had extended its research to the problems of high-altitude and space flight.

President Eisenhower and his advisors became convinced that the United States would make faster progress if more of the scientists could work together to solve the problems of exploring space. In April, 1958, the President asked Congress to set up the National Aeronautics and Space Agency (NASA). This new agency was to take over the work of the National Advisory Committee for Aeronautics and be responsible for the civilian space science and exploration program.

The National Aeronautics and Space Act was passed by Congress on July 29, 1958. The act declared: "It is the policy of the United States that activities in space should be devoted to peaceful purposes for the benefit of mankind."

In October the National Aeronautics and Space Administration was established. Dr. T. Keith Glennan, the president of the Case Institute of Technology, was named administrator. From the National Advisory Committee for Aeronautics NASA inherited 8,000 employees and five research centers. These centers included the Langley Laboratory at Langley Air Force Base, Virginia, which studied aircraft and missile structures; the Ames Aeronautical Laboratory at Moffett Naval Air Station in California, which studied the problems of high-speed flight; the Lewis Flight Propulsion Laboratory at Cleveland, Ohio, which worked on engines for airplanes and spaceships; the High Speed Flight Station at Edwards Air Force Base, California, where experiments with manned rockets were under way; and Wallops Island, Virginia, which tested rocket-powered vehicles. At Greenbelt, Maryland, NASA built a sixth laboratory, the Goddard Space Flight Center, named for the rocket pioneer.

NASA's space research began at once. It took over the Vanguard project from the Navy, and the Army's Huntsville laboratories became part of NASA along with Dr. von Braun and 5,500 employees. During its first year, NASA sent three rockets loaded with instruments deep into space. It put three new satellites into orbit. It worked with the rocket-powered X-15 aircraft and conducted tests with new rockets and satellites.

All this was part of NASA's broad research and development program aimed at furthering the exploration of space, first with unmanned and then with manned space vehicles. Their complete schedule called for exploration at an ever increasing distance from the earth —first to the moon, then to the planets Mars and Venus, and finally to the outer planets. The important first step, the achievement upon which NASA's entire program depended, was the placing of a manned space capsule into orbit around the earth. This became NASA's Project Mercury. Project Mercury would open the way to the moon and the planets.

In the fall of 1958 a group of engineers and scientists received the most challenging, and the most interesting, assignment to come out of the new space age. Their job was to send a manned space capsule into orbit around the earth, study the man's ability to live and work in space, and then return the man and the capsule safely back to earth. The engineers and scientists were members of the Space Task Group which the new National Aeronautics and Space Administration organized when just four days old. Under the direction of Robert R. Gilruth, the Space Task Group was to work on NASA's vitally important Project Mercury.

The men of the Space Task Group were well chosen for the tremendous challenge that lay ahead of them. For some time they had been studying the problems of space flight at the Langley Aeronautical and Lewis Flight Propulsion laboratories. Even though there had been no immediate prospect of sending a man into space, they had made a start at getting him there.

Serious work on plans for space flight had gotten under way in the United States early in 1956. At that time the Air Force began studying the problem of recovering a manned space capsule after it had been sent into orbit around the earth. The Air Force also began to develop space capsules that could be used for preliminary tests with animals.

The Army worked out a plan for sending a manned space capsule up about 150 miles, using the Redstone rocket. Recovery was to be by parachute. The Navy proposed sending a man into orbit in a collapsible pneumatic glider. The glider was to be launched in the nose of a giant rocket. Once in orbit, the glider would be inflated and flown down to a water landing by its pilot.

At the same time the men who were to form the Space Task Group were working on the many problems involved in putting a manned satellite into orbit. They worked on the best design for a space capsule and the development of a more powerful booster rocket.

All this study and planning for space flight had been carried on with very little money and no definite program for putting a man into space. But scientists were sure it would be done eventually, so they had gone ahead with some of the preliminary work. Then came the successful launching of the Soviet Sputnik. Suddenly, putting a man into space became the most important project of the newly established National Aeronautics and Space Administration. To get the program into operation, the agency was allotted $46,416,330 for research and development expenses and $2,425,000 for construction and equipment. Things were moving ahead at last!

Top. Robert R. Gilruth (second from right), first director of the Space Task Group, conducts a news conference. With him (left to right) are Virgil Grissom, Rear Admiral John Chew, and Walter C. Williams. Bottom. A huge Atlas rocket leaves the assembly line in San Diego, California. After final checkout, it will be flown to Cape Canaveral.

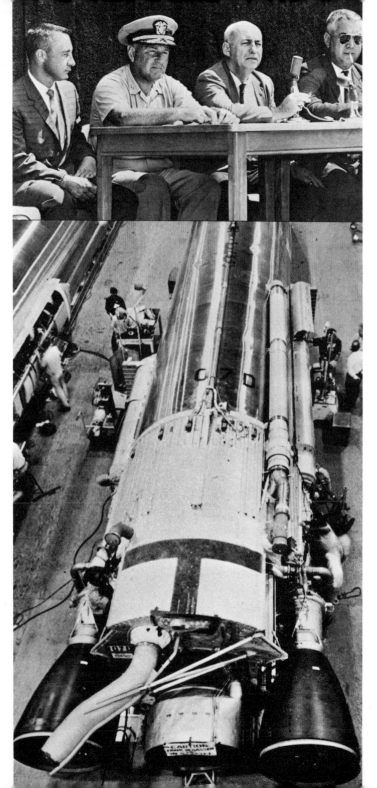

The men of the Space Task Group went to work at the Langley Research Center. Their objective was to put a man into orbit around the earth as soon as possible, but not before it was safe for him to go. They intended to make orbital flight no more risky than testing a new type of airplane.

The many factors involved in a successful space flight were divided among the members of the Space Task Group. Some worked on the problems of launching and recovery. Others were concerned with the rocket boosters, others with the numerous things that had to go into a space capsule to make sure its passenger survived his trip. To help them the members of the group had the advice of doctors who had specialized in space medicine. They could also call on the rest of NASA, the armed services, the universities, and industry. Project Mercury was the United States' first step toward interplanetary space flight. The lessons learned from its successful execution would determine what we could do next and how soon we could do it. Everyone was willing to help.

How long would it take for Project Mercury to put a man into orbit around the earth? The Space Task Group couldn't say for sure. To save time they planned to make as much use as possible of the equipment already available. They would use the Air Force's Atlas missile to boost their capsule up into space. (The Atlas was the only missile the United States had developed that was powerful enough to do the job.) To get their capsule into and out of orbit, they would use the simplest method that could be relied on to work. But they would still have to proceed slowly and carefully.

The men of the Space Task Group knew that they weren't the only ones working on the problem of putting a man into orbit around the earth. The scientists of the Soviet Union were doing the same thing. Although the United States naturally wanted to be the first to achieve manned space flight, Project Mercury was based on the fact that the safety of the astronaut was of the utmost importance. The Space Task Group could take no short cuts that might endanger the astronaut's life. Everything that went into Project Mercury would be tested over and over again.

A great many things were going into Project Mercury. There was the space capsule to be lifted high above the earth by an Atlas launch vehicle. After the capsule had circled the earth three times, it would have to be slowed down and returned to earth. All this would be accomplished while radio contact was being maintained with the capsule and a vast tracking network following its flight. Once the capsule began to descend, ships and planes would have to watch for it.

The object of all this care and attention, the man inside the capsule, would have to be protected in every way possible from the hostile space environment through which he traveled. In case something went wrong, he would have to be snatched from his capsule. If all went well, the effects of his journey would be studied with greatest care. From launch to landing his reactions would be recorded. In that way the Space Task Group would learn things to help prepare for future space flights. And, finally, detailed plans would have to be made for picking up the astronaut very quickly when he landed, because he would be coming down in the Atlantic Ocean.

Although these problems seemed to be enough to keep the members of the Space Task Group busy for a long, long time, they hoped Project Mercury would take no more than two or three years to put a man into orbit around the earth and bring him back.

V. THE EQUIPMENT FOR EXPLORING SPACE

"It looks like a big television tube!" That's what is said most often about the Project Mercury space capsule developed to carry a man around the earth. Tailored to fit the Atlas missile, it isn't very large—only six feet across at its wide end and ten feet long. But it is strong! Its double walls can stand up under the stress of accelerating to a speed of 18,000 miles an hour. Friction heat up to 2,000 degrees won't melt them.

The immense amount of heat that would be generated when a space craft reëntered the earth's atmosphere was the biggest problem faced by space-capsule designers. Aerodynamic experts began by experimenting with the streamlined shapes which worked well with high-speed aircraft. But when these sleek, needle-nosed shapes were used for space vehicles, they promptly burned up when they met the friction of the earth's atmosphere on the return trip. Streamlining reduced air resistance, but it also seemed to trap heat along the sides of the vehicle. A space craft, traveling much faster than an airplane, trapped so much heat that it burned.

It was NASA aerodynamics expert, H. Julien Allen, who solved the problem. He reasoned that a streamlined shape was the worst possible one for a space capsule. It should be exactly the opposite—blunt or stubby. Then heat would be bounced back into the atmosphere in the form of shock waves instead of collecting along the sides of the capsule. Allen's idea worked so well that a blunt shape became standard for space vehicles.

As a further protection against heat, a special shield was built over the blunt end of the Mercury capsule. The shield is coated with a resinous glass fiber which vaporizes when it gets hot, carrying away heat in the process.

The blunt end of the capsule serves still another purpose. It helps to slow the capsule down on its return journey. Eighteen thousand miles an hour is much too fast for a landing!

Opposite the blunt end of the capsule, in the narrow top portion, are stored the parachutes used in landing. A small chute called a drogue opens at 21,000 feet and a larger one lowers the capsule the rest of the way, landing it on the water as gently as possible. There is a third reserve chute in case it is needed. This is an example of the way much of the capsule's equipment is duplicated as an extra safeguard for the astronaut.

Towering above the capsule is the escape system. Booster rockets, such as the Atlas, are getting progressively more reliable, but every now and then something does go wrong. A rocket blows up on the launching pad; it goes off course; it doesn't reach the right alti-

Top. *H. Julien Allen, the aerodynamics expert who conceived of a blunt-shaped capsule.* Bottom. *View of a Mercury space capsule showing the escape rocket atop the spaceship.*

tude. What happens to the astronaut then? He must be gotten out of the way in a hurry! His capsule is blasted clear of the malfunctioning booster rocket by another, smaller rocket mounted in a 16-foot, orange-colored tower attached to the top of the capsule.

The escape rocket is a powerful, solid-fuel-burning device that can lift the capsule 2,500 feet into the air. It lifts it, not straight up, but slightly to one side so that it will be clear of the malfunctioning rocket below.

The key to a successful escape is speedy action. An electronic watch is kept on the booster rocket. As soon as something goes wrong, an automatic signal goes out to the escape rocket, which then lifts the capsule out of the danger area. If the automatic firing system doesn't work, the men monitoring the launching can start the escape rocket on its way. If all else fails, the astronaut himself can push a switch and start the escape procedure. He has only a few seconds, but the system is designed to work quickly. A series of clamps holding the capsule to the booster snap open. The escape rocket fires, and the capsule is up and away from the danger area. When a safe altitude is reached, a parachute lowers the capsule back to earth.

The important part of the capsule is the enclosure, or cockpit, for the astronaut. It is small; there is just enough room for the astronaut and all the instruments needed to keep track of him and his space craft.

The entire bottom of the capsule—the six-foot, blunt end—is occupied by the astronaut's couch. This is a fiber-glass and foam-rubber support especially designed to help the astronaut withstand the strains of launching and reëntry into the earth's atmosphere.

The instrument panel is located directly in front of the astronaut as he lies strapped to his couch. He can also use a periscope or look out of a small window without moving his head. There are times during flight when it would be difficult, or even impossible, for him to move more than his eyes. The capsule control stick is located near his right hand. The motion of the capsule can be directed with this one, single-hand control.

The capsule's door is a small hatch through which the astronaut must crawl. Once he is inside and the hatch is sealed, the atmosphere in the capsule is pressurized, cooled, and dehumidified.

As complicated and as wonderful as the Mercury capsule is, it was developed in a very short time. From the studies that had already been made of space vehicles, the new NASA Space Task Group had a good idea of what would be needed. Within a matter of weeks the McDonnell Aircraft Corporation had signed a contract to design, build, and develop a capsule for the Space Task Group.

Every part of the capsule was tested and tested again. Small-scale models were observed in wind tunnels and during flight. McDonnell turned out full-size "boilerplate" models made of sheet metal, which were used to test the various capsule mechanisms. Sometimes everything worked as it should, and sometimes

there was failure. Then the Space Task Group and Mc-
Donnell technicians would have to figure out what went
wrong and try again.

One of the most spectacular failures, for those who
were watching, was the November, 1960, test firing in
which the rocket lifted off the launching pad and then
dropped back. Within seconds the air was filled with
parachutes, smoke, and flame as the capsule's parachutes were released and its escape rocket fired.

It was discovered later that a malfunction had shut
off the booster rocket's engines just as it was leaving
the launching pad. The escape rocket received the same
signal it would have received if the booster had exhausted its fuel in space and shut down on schedule, so
the escape rocket fired just as it would have done miles
above the earth. But since the capsule was surrounded
by air instead of space, another control device released
the parachutes which would have eased its descent
through the atmosphere. All this time the capsule,
sending out the signals and flashing the lights that
would be used during a normal descent, was still sit-
ting on the launching pad.

Test failures such as this delayed Project Mercury for
days and weeks until everything that went wrong could
be located and corrected. But each correction made the
men of the Space Task Group all the more certain that
everything would work perfectly when an astronaut finally rode in the Mercury capsule.

The Atlas missile chosen to boost the Mercury capsule
into orbit was developed by the Air Force as an inter-

*Top. Technicians subject a new capsule to hundreds of hours
of careful checkout procedures. Bottom. A Mercury capsule
is lowered onto an Atlas rocket in preparation for a test firing.*

continental ballistic missile or ICBM. A ballistic missile is one that contains pre-set controls which keep it on its course. A guided missile, on the other hand, is controlled by radio from the ground. All missiles are propelled by rocket engines, and the term "rocket" is often used to designate the entire missile.

The Atlas has three powerful engines. Two are boosters that blast for 150 seconds after being ignited. They then drop off and the third engine continues. The three engines develop a combined total of 360,000 pounds of thrust. The Redstone rocket used in some of the Mercury test firings delivers a thrust of only 78,000 pounds, not enough to put the ton-and-a-half Mercury capsule into orbit. It is the Atlas' third stage that lifts the capsule to the proper altitude for orbit.

The Atlas is more than 70 feet high. That makes it taller than an average seven-story building. It is about ten feet in diameter. This sounds big, but all the space is needed. Inside its frame the missile carries fuel tanks for kerosene and liquid oxygen, a complicated system of fuel controls and tubes, and a guidance system capable of directing it to a point as much as 9,000 miles away.

Work on the Atlas, which is manufactured by General Dynamics Astronautics, began in 1951. But the missile wasn't fired with any great success until 1958, the year it was used to broadcast the President's Christmas message. It became operational, or ready for use as a weapon by the Air Force, in the summer of 1959.

There is now a whole family of Atlas missiles—the

Atlas-Able, the Atlas-Agena-A, the Atlas-Agena-B, the Atlas Centaur, and the Atlas-D. Designed for different purposes, they have the same first stage, but their second- and third-stage rockets differ. The one chosen for Project Mercury, the Atlas-D, has undergone more testing than the others because of the nature of its mission. The Atlas has thousands of parts, any one of which can go wrong, so not all the tests have been successful. The performance of the Atlas-D has been good enough, however, to win the confidence of the men chosen to ride it up into space.

A big part of Project Mercury never leaves the ground. The Space Task Group had to arrange for a vast array of people and instruments to watch over the launching of the capsule, its flight around the earth, and finally its landing in the Atlantic.

A control center was set up at Cape Canaveral, where the Mercury launchings were to take place. The men assigned there, all Mercury experts, would decide when the countdown should begin, when it should be held up, and even if the space shot should be called off altogether. They would follow the launching carefully, using television and instrument readings to check on what was happening to the Atlas, the capsule, and the astronaut. Once the capsule went into orbit they would continue to follow its progress and to talk with the astronaut by radio.

The Space Task Group also had to arrange for other groups of experts to monitor the Mercury capsule's

At the Cape Canaveral Control Center the orbital flight track-ing stations are plotted on an enormous board.

flight along the path it would follow as it circled the earth. This was the tracking network set up so that at no time on his journey would the man in the capsule be out of contact with men on the earth. At some of the 18 tracking stations there had to be equipment to bring the capsule down in case of trouble. All of them had to be able to track the capsule, collect information about it, and communicate with the astronaut. In addition to Cape Canaveral, Project Mercury tracking stations were planned for Bermuda, the Canary Islands, a ship in the Atlantic, two places in Africa, a ship in the Indian Ocean, two places in Australia, Canton Island in the Pacific Ocean, Hawaii, Southern California, Mexico, New Mexico, Texas, and an air base in Florida. Two additional stations on Grand Bahama and Grand Turk islands in the Atlantic would track the capsule during launching and recovery.

Finally, the Space Task Group had to plan for the successful recovery of the capsule and the astronaut from the Atlantic when the flight was over. Arrangements were made to have ships, airplanes, and helicopters deployed in all the places where the landing might take place—many of them in the area where the landing was planned and fewer where a landing was less likely. The recovery planes and ships had to be equipped with radar and other devices for locating the capsule. The capsule itself was to be equipped with a radio, yellow water dyes, smoke flares, and depth charges to attract the attention of searchers.

As much care went into the development of the

earth-bound portion of Project Mercury as went into the capsule. The Control Center, the tracking network, and the recovery forces would play an important part in bringing the astronaut back alive. And Project Mercury definitely intended to bring him back safely.

VI. CHOOSING THE MERCURY ASTRONAUT

MEN WANTED FOR TRAINING PROGRAM. *Must be gradu-ates of military test pilot school with at least 1,500 hours flying experience. Bachelor degree or equivalent in en-gineering or science required. Under 40 years of age and not more than 5 feet, 11 inches tall.*

This ad never appeared, but it lists some of the require-ments NASA's Space Task Group drew up for the man who was going to take that all-important first trip into space.

Just what would make a good spaceman? That was a difficult question for Project Mercury officials to answer. There were no spacemen to study for good and bad qualities. And no one knew for sure just what would be required of a spaceman as he traveled around the earth. One thing was certain—he would have to be a man willing to face the unknown and able to deal with any problems it might present.

The Space Task Group didn't have much time to de-cide what kind of a man to look for and where to find

him. As soon as Project Mercury got under way in the fall of 1958, it was imperative that a group of astronauts be selected and their training begun. They were going to do more than ride in the completed capsule; they were going to have a big part in the development of the Mercury program.

Beyond a doubt there were thousands of young men in the United States who would make good spacemen. The problem was to find those who would make the *best* spacemen and find them as quickly as possible. They would be the ones in the best physical condition; they would have the best mental attitude toward space flight; and they would have the best technical background.

One special group of men seemed to be a good source from which to choose. They were the nation's military test pilots. They had the necessary engineering training and experience with fast, high-flying aircraft. As test pilots they had already demonstrated that they could perform under difficult conditions.

Not all the test pilots in the United States are in the Air Force, Navy, or Marine Corps. Some very good ones test new planes and new equipment for aircraft companies. The Space Task Group, however, decided to consider only military test pilots because they could be easily transferred to Project Mercury. Their regular pay and allowances would continue, and they were already accustomed to a military way of life. And, an important point, complete records on them were available for Project Mercury officials.

As a test pilot, John Glenn made a record flight from California to New York (3 hours, 23 minutes, 8.4 seconds) while trying out an F8FU Crusader jet on March 9, 1955.

Hundreds of these records were examined by an NASA selection board late in 1958. Some basic requirements had already been settled. The men chosen could be no more than 5 feet, 11 inches tall. The size of the capsule made this rule necessary. The selection board also agreed that 1,500 hours of flying time would produce an experienced pilot, and they felt that the educational requirements must provide for the necessary technical background.

The records were studied with the greatest care. When the job was finished in January, 1959, one hundred and ten men had survived the initial screening. The main reason for elimination was lack of enough technical experience. Even so, the selection was difficult. The test pilots were an extremely well-qualified group of men.

An even more difficult selection lay ahead. For out of the initial 110 must be chosen the very best of the best. The men were divided into three groups for personal interviews.

The pilots came to Washington from all over the country. Their travel orders didn't tell them very much, but they soon found out what the trip was all about. They were thoroughly briefed on Project Mercury— what it had already done, what it hoped to do. Then they were asked, "Would you like to volunteer to be the man Project Mercury will send into space?"

It was expected that not every pilot would say yes, and not all of them did. Some were already deeply involved in important projects they didn't want to leave. Some had other reasons for saying no. The amazing thing, however, was the number who did say yes. Of the first 69 pilots who were asked, no less than 55 volunteered for Project Mercury.

With so many highly qualified candidates on hand there was no need to call in the rest of the 110 test pilots. In fact the number of candidates had to be reduced to 32. This was done through a series of interviews and advanced aptitude tests. The men were questioned about their knowledge of engineering, their military background, their childhood, their likes and dislikes. Once again the very best of the best were chosen.

But even 32 highly qualified men were more than Project Mercury could use. It had been decided to limit the final selection to seven. Then each one could be assigned a different part of the Mercury program as an area of specialization. A final series of tests would have to reduce the 32 to 7.

The tests began at the Lovelace Clinic in Albuquerque, New Mexico. In groups of six or seven the thirty-two candidates went to Albuquerque where they were given the most thorough physical examinations possible. For seven and one-half days they were probed and prodded. They were x-rayed, their brain waves measured, their eyes were examined. They were immersed in a tank of water so their specific gravity could be determined. Their hearts, circulatory systems, stomachs, muscles, bones, and glands were all checked with the greatest care. Since they were test pilots, all of these men were naturally required to be in good physical condition. The doctors were looking for those who were in the very best physical condition.

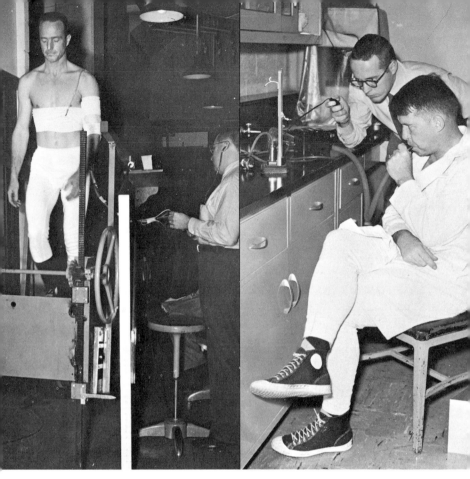

Left. *Navy Lieutenant Scott Carpenter walks a treadmill as part of his heart test.* Right. *To measure his lung capacity, Walter Schirra blows through a hose to see how long he can hold up the column of mercury in the tube at left.*

Albuquerque was only the beginning. From the Lovelace Clinic the candidates went to Wright Patterson Air Force Base at Dayton, Ohio. There they underwent another series of tests—this time to measure how well they performed under stress. Not one of these tests was very comfortable. The men had to spend two hours in a heat chamber with the temperature at 130 degrees Fahrenheit. They were spun around in a centrifuge, placed in a pressure chamber, in a dark soundproof room, in an ice bath. They walked on treadmills, rode on tilt tables, stepped up twenty inches to a platform every two seconds for five minutes.

During these tests the candidates were studied to see how well they performed in difficult or confusing situations. Then they moved on to the last series of tests—psychological, intelligence, and aptitude. In this part of the screening process they took a "self-inventory" examination in which they answered 566 questions about themselves. They were also interviewed by psychiatrists and took several standard written tests.

When it was all over, the exhausted candidates went home. They were, without a doubt, the most tested men that ever lived, and the Project Mercury selection board was faced with the task of evaluating the results of all those tests.

The half-dozen men on the board were all medical or technical experts. The candidates were unknown to them. From the beginning, numbers had been used instead of the names of the men being considered. The final selection would be based strictly on the records now before the board.

It would have been easy to choose more than seven men. The results of the tests showed that many of the candidates were truly superior, both mentally and physically. The choice of only seven was a difficult one. Once again it was a matter of picking the very best from a group of highly qualified individuals. It was important that no possible flaw in any of the candidates be overlooked. The success of Project Mercury would depend on the seven who were chosen.

In general, what were the men like whose records were before the Project Mercury selection board? Their ages ranged from 28 to 38; all were married. Only two had lived in large cities before going to college, and 20 were only, or eldest, children. They were comfortable, mature, adaptable men with lots of drive. They were intelligent. Their intelligence scores ranged from 130 to 141 (a score of 100 is average).

Most of the candidates had entered military service during World War II. Their attitudes toward flying varied. Some of them had wanted to fly from an early age; others had had the average boy's interest in airplanes. About half of the group had volunteered for test-pilot training. The rest had been selected for the job because of their accomplishments in some other field. They did not consider their work unduly dangerous. For them, knowledge and caution were a big part of safe flying.

Their reasons for volunteering for Project Mercury? They considered it an important undertaking and wanted to be part of it. They felt that space flight was the next step in the progress of aviation. The man who

(Left to right) Astronauts Carpenter, Cooper, Glenn, Grissom, Schirra, Shepard and Slayton—the first seven to be trained as American spacemen.

said, "There aren't many new frontiers. This is a chance to be in on one of them," spoke for the whole group.

These, then, were the men from whom the seven Mercury astronauts were to be chosen. Their test results were studied and studied again. Then the selection board looked at the past-performance record of each man and considered what special abilities he had that might prove valuable to Project Mercury.

Finally the choice was made—Malcolm Scott Carpenter, Leroy Gordon Cooper, Jr., John Herschel Glenn, Jr., Virgil Ivan Grissom, Walter Marty Schirra, Jr., Alan Bartlett Shepard, Jr., and Donald Kent Slayton.

VII. THE MERCURY ASTRONAUTS

Malcolm Scott Carpenter

One of the astronauts was beginning a tour of duty as an intelligence officer aboard the anti-submarine aircraft carrier *U.S.S. Hornet* when he was selected for Project Mercury. He was 33-year-old Navy Lieutenant Malcolm Scott Carpenter, who had just graduated from the Navy's Air Intelligence School in Washington, D.C.

Scott Carpenter's home town is Boulder, Colorado. After finishing high school there, he enrolled in the Navy's flight training program at Colorado College. He had progressed to primary flight training at Ottumwa, Iowa, when World War II ended. Carpenter returned to Colorado, where he studied aeronautical engineering at the state university. After graduating in 1949, he went back to the Navy and flight training. This time he won his wings of gold.

Following duty with Patrol Squadron 6 during the Korean conflict, Carpenter attended the Navy Test Pilot School. Then came several years of flight-testing Navy aircraft. He worked with the new jet fighters, the A-3D Skywarrior, the F-11F Tiger, and the F-9F Cougar. His assignment to the Naval Air Intelligence School followed, and then Project Mercury. At the time of his selection, Carpenter had no way of knowing he would be the second astronaut to complete an orbital flight around the earth.

Astronaut Carpenter is 5 feet 10½ inches tall and weighs 160 pounds. He has green eyes and brown hair and is a quiet, thoughtful person. He is the father of four children, two girls and two boys. His favorite sports are archery, water skiing, and skin diving.

Most of Carpenter's flying has been in multi-engine planes. When he was selected for Project Mercury he had 2,800 hours of flying time, but only 300 hours of this was spent in jets—the least of any of the astronauts.

Leroy Gordon Cooper

The youngest of the astronauts also was the one to fly a plane at the youngest age. Leroy Gordon Cooper was only eight when he took over the controls for the first time. At 16 he had made his first solo flight. Flying was in his blood. His father was an Air Force officer and pilot, and young Leroy grew up with flyers and airplanes.

He was born March 6, 1927, in Shawnee, Oklahoma, and went to grade and high school there. When he graduated from high school in 1945, Leroy joined the Marine Corps. After his discharge a year later, he resumed his education at the University of Hawaii.

In 1949 Leroy Cooper was back in uniform. He had received a reserve officer's commission in the Army; this was transferred to the Air Force and the Air Force called him for flight training. After receiving his pilot's wings, Cooper went to Germany, where he flew the F-84 and F-86 jet fighters.

When he returned home, the Air Force sent him to school. He received a degree in aeronautical engineering from the Air Force Institute of Technology at Dayton, Ohio.

The Air Force Experimental Flight Test School came next and then an assignment testing experimental aircraft at Edwards Air Force Base in California. There he flew some of the Air Force's highest flying and fastest planes. In all he had some 2,300 hours of flying time—1,400 of it in jets.

Astronaut Cooper is 5 feet 9½ inches tall and weighs 150 pounds. He has blue eyes and close-cropped brown hair and a lean appearance. He is fond of outdoor sports, especially riding, hunting, and fishing. He has two daughters who like to go hiking with their father.

Cooper was a captain in the Air Force at the time of his selection.

John Herschel Glenn, Jr.

The oldest of the seven astronauts, and the first actually to orbit the earth, is green-eyed, red-haired John Herschel Glenn, Jr. He was 37 and a lieutenant colonel in the Marine Corps when selected for Project Mercury. John

Glenn grew up and went to high school in New Concord, Ohio, where his father operated a plumbing and heating business. When John graduated from high school in 1939, he became a student at New Concord's Muskingum College. He was a back on Muskingum's football team, the only one of the astronauts to engage in a major varsity sport.

The Japanese attack on Pearl Harbor brought a temporary halt to John Glenn's education. He enlisted in the naval aviation cadet program in March, 1942. He graduated a year later and chose to serve with the Marine Corps.

After the future astronaut won his wings in 1943, he was sent to the Marshall Islands in the Pacific as a member of Marine Fighter Squadron 155. He took part in 59 combat missions against the Japanese, flying the Corsair, one of the best fighter planes used in the Pacific theater.

When the war ended, John Glenn decided to remain in the Marine Corps. He had assignments in China, Guam, and the United States. During the Korean conflict he flew with both the Marines and the Air Force— a total of 90 combat missions during which he shot down three MIGs in nine days. He was awarded five Distinguished Flying Crosses and the Air Medal with 18 clusters for his service in World War II and in Korea.

After the Korean conflict was over, John Glenn became a test pilot. In his new job he worked with a number of advanced Navy aircraft. In one of them, the F-8U, he set a transcontinental speed record in 1957—

Left to right.
Malcolm Scott Carpenter
Leroy Gordon Cooper, Jr.
John Herschel Glenn, Jr.
Virgil Ivan Grissom
Walter Marty Schirra, Jr.
Alan Bartlett Shepard, Jr.
Donald Kent Slayton

Los Angeles to New York in 3 hours and 23 minutes. At the time he became a Mercury astronaut Glenn had more than 5,000 hours of flying time, 1,500 of it in jet aircraft.

Astronaut Glenn is 5 feet 10½ inches tall; he weighs 165 pounds. A strict program of diet and exercise brought him down from the 180 pounds he weighed when he was selected, and he continues to exercise regularly. His favorite sports are aquatic ones, boating and water skiing. He has a son and a daughter.

Virgil Ivan Grissom

The second American astronaut to take a ride through space, Virgil Grissom, is from Mitchell, Indiana, where he was born in 1926. He started Air Force flight training as soon as he finished high school in 1944, but the war ended before he could finish. His short military career over, Grissom enrolled at Purdue University to study mechanical engineering. Four years later, when he graduated, he resumed his interrupted flight training. He won his wings in March, 1951, in time to fly a hundred combat missions in Korea in the F-86 Sabre-jet fighter.

After Korea, Grissom became a flight instructor. In 1955 the Air Force sent him back to school for a year to study aeronautical engineering at its Institute of Technology located at Wright Patterson Air Force Base, Dayton, Ohio. Then he went to the test pilot school at

Edwards Air Force Base. His assignment as a test pilot returned him to Wright Patterson, where he tested fighter planes. He had over 3,000 hours of flying time, more than 2,000 of it in jets.

Astronaut Grissom, who is called "Gus" by his friends, is 5 feet 7 inches tall and weighs 155 pounds. He has brown eyes and brown hair, which he wears cut short. He has a quiet, reserved manner and a sharp sense of humor. His hobbies are hunting and fishing. He has two sons.

Grissom, who was captain in the Air Force at the time of selection, almost didn't get to be an astronaut. He has chronic hay fever. When the doctors at the Lovelace Clinic were ready to disqualify him, Grissom successfully argued that there would be no ragweed pollen in space. And for good measure he would be sealed in a pressurized cabin. With his physical examinations safely behind him, he went on to do extremely well in the stress tests. The ability to stay calm in an emergency, which had made him a good test pilot, helped him to become an astronaut.

Walter Marty Schirra, Jr.

When he was called to Washington to be interviewed for Project Mercury, Walter Marty Schirra, Jr., was working with one of the Navy's newest planes, the twin-jet McDonnell F-4H fighter. For a while he hesitated about volunteering for Project Mercury, because he felt that the Navy's jet development program was an important one, too. However, after thinking it over, he decided that he could make a greater contribution as an astronaut, and his answer was yes. He would volunteer for Project Mercury.

Schirra's interest in flying began at an early age. His father was a World War I flyer and, after the war, he became a barnstorming pilot who traveled around the eastern part of the United States giving flying exhibitions in a light plane.

Walter Schirra, Jr. was born March 12, 1923, in Hackensack, New Jersey. After attending grade and high school and one year of engineering college in New Jersey, he won an appointment to the United States Naval Academy.

After his graduation in 1945, Schirra served at sea for a few years before he applied for flight training. He won his wings at Pensacola, Florida, and became a Navy fighter pilot.

When the Korean conflict broke out, Schirra was an exchange pilot with the Air Force's 154th Fighter Bomber Squadron. His 90 combat missions in Korea were with this squadron. Flying a F-84 jet fighter, he downed one MIG and possibly another.

Back again with the Navy, Schirra worked with the Sidewinder missile and the Navy's new F-7U3 Cutlass and F-J3 Fury jet fighters before entering test-pilot training. When he became an astronaut, 1,700 of his 3,000 flying hours were in jets.

A lieutenant commander in the Navy at the time of

his selection, Schirra is an easy-going, relaxed person, fond of sport cars, hi-fi, and skiing, both on water and on snow. He is 5 feet 10 inches tall and weighs 185 pounds. He has two children, a boy and a girl.

Alan Bartlett Shepard

America's first spaceman, Astronaut Alan Bartlett Shepard, is a Navy man like Schirra. Before his selection for Project Mercury, he was a lieutenant commander serving as an aircraft readiness officer on the staff of the commander of the Atlantic Fleet.

Astronaut Shepard was born November 18, 1923, in East Derry, New Hampshire. He went to school there and spent a year at the Admiral Farragut Academy in Toms River, New Jersey, before entering the United States Naval Academy.

After his graduation from Annapolis in 1944, Shepard spent the last year of the war on the destroyer *Cogswell* in the Pacific. He then entered flight training, receiving his pilot's wings in March, 1947. Following duty in this country and in the Mediterranean as a fighter pilot, Shepard was sent to test-pilot school. As a test pilot he took part in high-altitude flights to study light at different levels and in different air masses. He also helped with the development of the Navy's in-flight refueling system and tested some of the Navy's new jet fighters. Almost half of his 3,600 hours of flying time had been in jets.

Shepard is 5 feet 11 inches tall and weighs 160 pounds. He has blue eyes and brown hair, which he wears in a crew cut. He is quick-witted and full of energy. He plays golf, likes ice skating and water skiing. He has two daughters.

Donald Kent Slayton

Donald Kent Slayton served with the Air Force in both combat theaters during World War II. He flew 56 combat missions as a B-25 pilot in Europe and, after a short period back home as an instructor, flew seven missions over Japan.

The future astronaut was born on March 1, 1924, in Sparta, Wisconsin, and graduated from high school there in 1942. He entered the Air Force as an aviation cadet and won his wings a year later.

After the war Slayton enrolled at the University of Minnesota to study aeronautical engineering. He got his degree in 1949 and went to work for the Boeing Aircraft Company in Seattle, Washington. When he was called back to active duty by the Air Force in 1951, Slayton decided to make the Air Force his career.

He was serving as a fighter pilot in Germany when he was assigned to the Air Force Flight Test Pilot School at Edwards Air Force Base. He stayed on at Edwards to become an experimental test pilot specializing in jet fighters. Of his 3,400 hours in the air, 2,000 have been in jets.

The blue-eyed, brown-haired Slayton was an Air Force captain when selected. He is 5 feet 10½ inches tall and weighs 160 pounds. Like the other astronauts he is fond of outdoor activities—hunting, fishing, and skiing in his case. He has one child, a son named Kent.

VIII. THE MERCURY ASTRONAUTS GET READY TO EXPLORE SPACE

"Gentlemen, these are the astronaut volunteers."

The speaker was Walter Bonney, the National Aeronautics and Space Administration's press chief. The place was NASA's Washington headquarters. The time was two o'clock on the afternoon of April 9, 1959. The final selection of the Mercury astronauts had been made a few days earlier; now they were being presented to the public for the first time.

Behind Mr. Bonney as he made his announcement sat Donald K. Slayton, Alan B. Shepard, Jr., Walter M. Schirra, Jr., Virgil I. Grissom, John H. Glenn, Jr., Leroy G. Cooper, Jr., and Malcolm S. Carpenter, seven poised young men in business suits. They were about to embark on an intensive period of training for manned space flight. One of them would be the first American to travel in space. All of them would play a big part in making Project Mercury a success.

A training headquarters for the astronauts had already been set up at Langley Field, an Air Force base in southern Virginia. Langley would be "home" to the astronauts, but they would spend considerable time in other places, working with the manufacturers of space equipment and using training devices not available at Langley. Carrying orders from the Air Force, the Navy, or the Marine Corps—orders which assigned them for duty with NASA on a full-time basis—the seven Project Mercury astronauts arrived at Langley to begin the most challenging job of their careers. Not only would they be learning to fly an entirely new type of craft, they would also be helping to develop both the craft and the techniques for its operation.

Training at Langley began with a series of briefings in which members of the Space Task Group explained Project Mercury in detail. Each of the seven astronauts was assigned an area in which to specialize. Carpenter's was communications and navigational aids; Cooper was given the Redstone rocket to be used in suborbital shots. To Glenn went the job of helping to plan the space capsule's cockpit. The various automatic and manual devices for controlling the flight of the capsule were to be Grissom's specialty; Schirra's was the capsule's life-support system. Shepard was assigned to work with the plans for tracking and recovering the capsule, and to Slayton went the mighty Atlas booster that would lift the capsule into orbit.

A part of the astronauts' time at Langley was spent in "school." Because of the many demands that would be made on them during their training and during their rides through space, it was important that they have a good working knowledge of the basic sciences. Astron-

omy, physics, geography, and meteorology were given
to them in big doses. Experts lectured on such sub-
jects as aviation biology, ballistics, the principles of propulsion, and gyroscopic theory. For "home work" they
were given technical reports to study. Along with a
thorough understanding of the mechanics of space
travel, they were acquiring the knowledge they would
need to make detailed observations of themselves and
their surroundings while in space.

Not all of the astronauts' time was spent in the class-
room. They learned a great deal about space flight by
actually going through the procedures they would
someday use. They couldn't practice space flight in
space, of course, but they did the next best thing. They
used devices cleverly constructed to reproduce the conditions of space flight. These machines, called simulators, were first developed to help train airplane pilots,
and they had become almost uncanny in the way they
could make a man think he was actually flying an
airplane.

Developing simulators for space flight was a more
difficult process. Until the first space flight had actually been completed, there was no way of knowing for
sure just what conditions should be reproduced. One
of the most complicated of the simulators developed at
Langley is one to produce the effect of orbital flight
motion. An astronaut's couch is suspended in midair
before a circular motion picture screen. Reclining on
this couch as he would during a space flight, the astronaut, through a periscope, watches films as they are

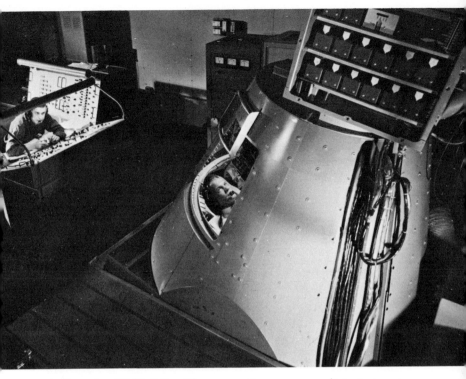

At Langley Field John Glenn practices space-craft instrument procedures in a training device that resembles a Mercury capsule.

projected on the screen. The films, taken by a missile, show the earth as it looks from 100 miles up in space. As he watches, the astronaut "flies" his capsule. He makes corrections with his control stick in accordance with the picture he gets of the earth. The couch floats on an air jet. Smaller jets, controlled by the astronaut's stick, change its attitude or direction. After hours of practice in this simulator, the astronaut wouldn't be afraid to maneuver his capsule if he wanted to get a better look at something while in space. And in the unlikely event that his instruments should fail, he would know that he could navigate by using his periscope to look at the earth below him.

Another simulator was developed to give the astronaut practice in maneuvering the space capsule during its turbulent reëntry into the earth's atmosphere. In this one the astronaut was placed in front of an instrument panel equipped with dials to indicate how straight and level his capsule was "flying." When the dials indicated a condition that needed correction—too much rolling motion, for example—he would have to correct it by using his control stick.

For some of their training the astronauts had to travel to Johnsville, Pennsylvania. There at the Navy's Acceleration Laboratory, they rode in a giant centrifuge which duplicated the acceleration and deceleration stresses the astronaut would have to endure during his space flight. Acceleration occurs when a moving object gains speed. If you have ridden in a jet airplane, you must have felt the effects of acceleration when the plane took off and

Top. An astronaut steps into the gondola suspended from the 50-foot arm of the Johnsville centrifuge. Bottom. His face contorted by acceleration stresses, Scott Carpenter struggles to work his control stick in the whirling centrifuge.

your body was forced back against the seat. Deceleration occurs when a moving object loses speed. When
you ride in a car that comes to a sudden stop, you feel
the effects of deceleration.

In the course of his trip through space, the astronaut
would experience rapid acceleration on take-off and
rapid deceleration on reëntry into the earth's atmosphere. If the booster rocket failed and the escape rocket
went into action, there would be violent acceleration as
the capsule shot away, followed by deceleration as it
slowed against the atmosphere.

The stresses the human body experiences during acceleration or deceleration are expressed in terms of g-
numbers. Gravity pulls everyone to the earth with a
force of one g. Since this pull is always present, we
never notice it. However, if it were to be doubled we
would experience difficulty in walking or climbing. At
three g's we wouldn't be able to walk or climb at all.
At four g's we could barely crawl, and five g's would
make it difficult to move even an arm. For each of
these g's we would be feeling a pull equal to the total
number of g's multiplied by our weight. If we weighed
100 pounds, at 5 g's we would experience a pull, or
force, of 500 pounds. No wonder we would be unable
to move!

The centrifuge at Johnsville gave the astronauts valuable experience under the stress of as many as 20 g's.
It also developed their ability to withstand the effects
of rapid acceleration or deceleration because they found

that, with practice, they could perform as well at 16 g's as they did during their first rides at 10 g's.

The Johnsville centrifuge is a pill-shaped gondola suspended at the end of a 50-foot arm. A 180-ton motor whirls the arm around at tremendous speeds. The gondola can be rotated to produce the effect of acceleration on take-off or deceleration on reëntry. Strapped to a supporting couch, the astronaut rides the ten-by-six-foot gondola. He wears his helmet and, for the more strenuous rides, his pressure suit.

When the centrifuge begins to whirl, the g's increase rapidly, as they do during an actual space flight. As they mount, the astronaut's heart rate and respiration are recorded. After the ride there are further checks to determine if the high g's have injured him in any way.

The gondola has the same instruments and controls as the Mercury capsule. During his ride the astronaut tries to do the things he would do if he were "flying" his capsule—speak into his microphone, read his instruments, manipulate his control stick—in spite of the stress of the high g forces. When the ride is all over and he gets out of the gondola, the astronaut is exhausted. His muscles are sore and he feels bruised, but he knows that he has successfully "flown" under the stress of higher g forces than he is likely to encounter in an actual space flight.

Another training device was located at NASA's Lewis Research Center in Cleveland. This was the Multiple

Axis Space Test Facility, or MASTIF, a machine developed to give the astronauts practice in controlling the capsule when it shot free of the burned-out booster rocket. An automatic control system would normally steady the capsule, but if it failed the astronaut would have to do the controlling himself.

MASTIF has three metal frameworks surrounding a chair in which the pilot sits. Each one of the three produces a different kind of tumbling motion. The rider can be spun in only one direction or he can be spun in three directions at once. The astronauts found spinning in one direction no problem, but spinning in three directions at the same time was something else again! They had to fight to focus their eyes on the control dial, to force themselves to read it, and then make the movements with the control stick that would gradually bring the spinning MASTIF to a halt. They emerged weak and wobbly from their ordeal but confident that, no matter how much their Mercury capsule tumbled about in space, they would be able to control it.

To prepare for the sensation of weightlessness they would encounter in space, the astronauts took a series of airplane rides in which they were weightless for periods as long as a minute. During orbital flights they would be weightless for several hours, but there was no way to keep them weightless that long without sending them up into space. Three kinds of planes were used, the Air Force C-131, C-135 and F-100F.

During the rides in the two-seater F-100F, the jet plane climbed to 40,000 feet. Then with the after-

Astronaut Grissom sits in the MASTIF chair, surrounded by three metal frameworks which can spin him in three directions at once.

burner on to give more power, down it went in a fast 30-degree dive to 25,000 feet. Then up it streaked again at full power until it reached the point where the climbing momentum of the plane canceled out the pull of gravity. For 60 seconds the plane and its occupants were weightless. During this time the astronaut had various tasks to perform. On some of his rides he practiced eating from squeeze bottles; on others he took short tests to see how well he could perform while weightless. When he got back on the ground there were more tests to see if he had suffered any ill effects from the short period of weightlessness. No problems at all developed during the rides, but there was no way of telling for sure what the result would be when the weightlessness lasted for four hours or more.

Another part of the Mercury flight—getting out of the capsule after it made its water landing—called for considerable practice beforehand. In a pool at Langley and later in the Gulf of Mexico, in calm water and in high waves, the seven astronauts got themselves out of a floating capsule. They had to release the straps holding them to their couch, unfasten the various hoses and wires running from their pressure suits, and remove part of the instrument panel to get to the escape hatch at the top of the capsule. Life raft and survival kit went through the hatch first, followed by the astronaut who then tied his inflated raft to the capsule to await rescue. A great deal of salt water was swallowed in these maneuvers, but the astronauts learned they could leave the capsule through the top hatch if they had to.

Three astronauts experience weightlessness during a zero gravity ride in a C-131 airplane.

The busy astronauts had still other forms of training. They spent hours in pressure chambers, in dark sound-proof rooms, and in steam rooms. And they did enough flying in the F-102 jet fighter to keep up their proficiency as pilots. The Mercury astronauts were going to be ready for that first trip into space.

IX. TEST SHOTS FOR PROJECT MERCURY

While the seven astronauts were spinning madly in the MASTIF or whirling around in the centrifuge, the Mercury capsule was undergoing tests, too. Through a series of trial shots it was moving closer and closer to the goal of Project Mercury—manned orbital flight. A special solid-fuel launch vehicle was developed to lift some of the early test capsules. Called Little Joe, it had a launch thrust of 250,000 pounds, enough to reach a fairly high altitude. Beginning in the fall of 1959, several Little Joes were used in tests designed primarily to check the operation of the capsule's escape system under various emergency conditions. Before an astronaut could be shot into space, the escape system had to be foolproof.

Most of the capsules launched with the Little Joes were development, or boilerplate, models. Next came tests with production-type capsules—the real thing—and with more powerful launch vehicles, the Redstone and Atlas boosters. The Redstone was the in-between booster. More powerful than the Little Joe, it still lacked the necessary thrust to put a capsule into orbit. The Atlas could do that. The Redstone was used to test Mercury capsules on short-range, ballistic flights up into space and back down again.

The first attempt to launch a capsule with a Redstone booster got nowhere at all. The Redstone rose about four inches and then settled back, acquiring some dents in the process. It had to be replaced. A month later, on December 19, 1960, the first Mercury-Redstone flight took off for space. It was a success although the capsule came down a little too fast.

The necessary adjustments were made, and the Mercury-Redstone combination was tried again. At Cape Canaveral, on January 31, 1961, a capsule was launched carrying a three-year-old chimpanzee named Ham. After a breakfast of baby cereal, condensed milk, half an egg, cooking oil and gelatin, Ham had been strapped to a specially designed contour couch. His arms were free because he had work to do. Above his couch was a system of lights and levers which Ham had been trained to use. A white light flashed when he pulled the correct lever, and he got a mild shock unless he pulled it every 20 seconds. To complicate things, a blue light flashed every two minutes warning him of an impending shock unless he pulled still another lever.

Ham was able to manipulate his levers successfully in spite of 6½ minutes of weightlessness and the force of 14.6 g's he encountered on the way back down. His trip in space lasted 18 minutes. However, a malfunction in the booster caused Ham to travel 421 miles—116

Top. *The first Mercury capsule successfully launched by a Redstone booster is lowered onto the deck of the USS Valley Forge.* Bottom. *Ham, the first chimpanzee sent into space, reaches out for an apple after his ride.*

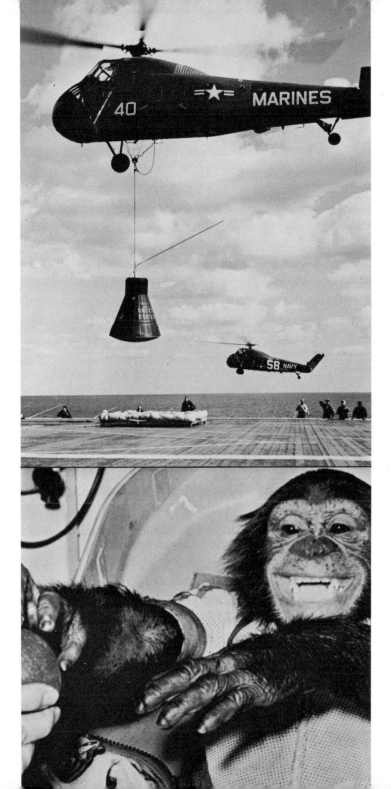

miles farther than had been planned. Consequently he overshot the recovery ships. To add to his troubles, his capsule keeled over and took on some water after it had been in the ocean awhile. A helicopter arrived before much damage was done, but a worried Ham emerged from the capsule after it had been lifted to the deck of the recovery ship. He was given an immediate checkup. The trip had not harmed him in any way, and after he had eaten an apple he felt much better.

The 37-pound Ham was the heaviest passenger the Mercury capsule had carried, but he wasn't the first. Two of the Little Joe rockets had lifted capsules carrying passengers, the rhesus monkeys Sam and Miss Sam. Both were safely recovered from the Atlantic after successful operation of the capsule escape system, an achievement that pleased Project Mercury officials and, no doubt, Sam and Miss Sam as well.

The Redstone flight that followed Ham's trip into space carried no passenger. His misadventures had indicated that some corrections would have to be made in both the booster and the capsule. This new flight was to insure that everything was now in good working order. It was, so Project Mercury could take another big step forward. A Redstone was used to lift a man into space. The man was Astronaut Alan Shepard and, as we have already seen, his space trip was an extremely successful step forward. The Redstone worked perfectly, and all the capsule's complicated systems performed in a satisfactory manner.

May 5, 1961, was a happy day for Project Mercury, but Shepard's one flight wasn't enough to insure that the capsule was absolutely reliable. A second manned flight would provide a better test. Preparations were made to send up one more Redstone-boosted capsule to duplicate Freedom 7's successful trip. There would be some changes. The next capsule would have a "picture" window and the astronaut would have more time to look around and observe his space environment.

Which one of the astronauts would go this time? It proved to be Virgil Grissom, one of the three men alerted for the Redstone flights. He had helped with the preparations for the May 5 flight. And two months later, on July 21, 1961, he was the man that climbed into the capsule for the second trial.

His trip started off smoothly enough. In fact it was smoother than Astronaut Shepard's, for the capsule had been modified to cut down the vibration that gave Shepard such a shaking at 36,000 feet. Grissom commented later: "This is one problem I feel we have licked."

He described the new window as "about like a key-hole to me, but it is a big window, anyway for a space flight." He began to look through it almost at once, watching the blue sky of the launching change to a pitch black as he gained altitude. And right in the center of the window he saw a star. That star cost the astronaut two steak dinners. He had bet John Glenn that they would not be able to see stars in flight. Shepard had seen none on his flight.

Like Shepard, Astronaut Grissom heard with considerable relief the sound of the escape rocket firing when the Redstone's engine cut off. Then he saw the escape tower shoot off to the right. The capsule's parachutes are located underneath the escape system. If the escape rocket doesn't fire, the parachutes can't be used. This would result in a hard landing. In describing the sound the escape rocket made as it fired, Grissom said: "It was really comforting."

There was a bright sun shining in the black sky—so bright, in fact, that at one point the astronaut was afraid he might be blinded by the light. The shaft of sunlight didn't reach his face, however, and he was able to go through the same procedures for controlling the motion of the capsule that Shepard had used.

The new window proved to be almost too much of an attraction. Grissom reported that he was so fascinated by what he could see—the horizon, the clouds, and the sky shading from a light blue to a deep black—that he had difficulty concentrating on his control maneuvers.

Soon it was time to fire the retro-rockets to slow the capsule. Grissom did this manually. Then he started down. He had a smooth descent. The g forces reached 10.2 as the capsule entered the earth's atmosphere—not enough, though, to cause him any difficulty. His parachutes came out on schedule; his landing was "a pretty good bump, but nothing that would jar me."

So far it was a very successful flight, but there was still time for things to go wrong. And they did.

The capsule fell over on its left side when it hit, but

Top. Virgil Grissom (left) and his alternate, John Glenn, eat an early morning breakfast before Grissom's flight. Bottom. In the Mercury Control Center astronauts Glenn, Schirra and Shepard intently follow Grissom's launch.

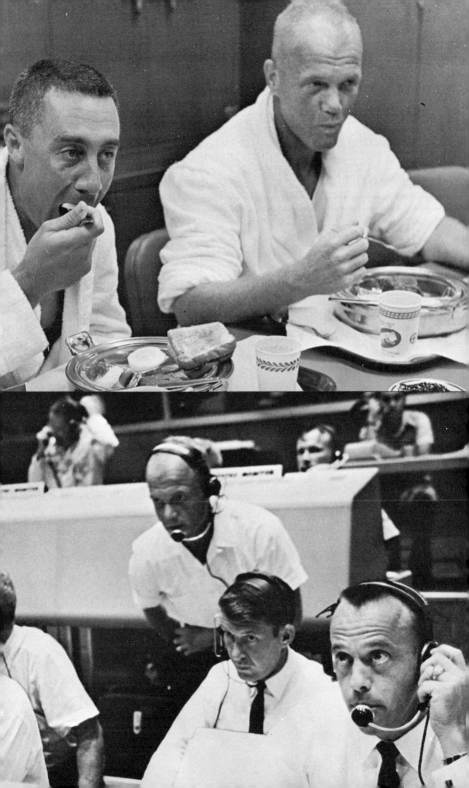

it soon righted itself. Grissom began recording the positions of his switches and gauges for later study at Cape Canaveral. He had already partially prepared himself for leaving the capsule—unfastened his straps, loosened his helmet, and disconnected most of the wires and lines running from his suit. Helicopters were standing by. When the astronaut was ready to be picked up, he notified them. While he waited, he removed the cover of the detonator that would blow the side hatch open, and pulled the safety pin. And then it happened. The hatch blew off! As Grissom described it later: "I was lying there, all in business, and pow, the hatch blew up and I looked up and saw nothing but blue sky and water started to come in over the sill."

One look was enough for him. He tossed off his helmet and got out. The helicopter pilot reported that Grissom followed immediately behind the door. It was almost one motion. The helicopter darted down toward the capsule hoping to get a line on it before it sank. Grissom, held up by his space suit, tried to help, but the wash from the helicopter's rotors blew him away.

The first helicopter on the scene had been joined by three others, but there was no saving the Liberty Bell 7, as Grissom's capsule had been named. The five-million-dollar, instrument-laden Liberty Bell 7 was full of water and too heavy to lift. Astronaut Grissom was in trouble, too. Water was coming in through an opening in his suit and he was beginning to sink. He was surrounded by helicopters but he couldn't get to any of them. Finally one of the chopper pilots got in close

Aboard the USS Randolph, Grissom jokingly empties the sea water from his boot after taking off his space suit.

enough to lower a sling. Grissom was picked up and taken to the waiting recovery ship *Randolph*.

Later when a reporter asked him if he had been frightened at any time during his space flight, Grissom replied with a grin: "I was scared." When he was asked whether space flight was as interesting as Astronaut Shepard had reported it to be, Grissom said: "It certainly was; I'd recommend the trip to anyone."

Astronaut Grissom had traveled 307 miles from Cape Canaveral. He had reached a height of 118 miles, and he had been weightless for five minutes. His was the last Mercury flight to use the Redstone rocket. The malfunctioning hatch door would have to be studied, but there were no more test objectives that could be achieved with the Redstone. The next step was orbital flight with the more powerful Atlas.

An attempt to place a Mercury capsule in orbit with the Atlas had failed on April 25, 1961. The rocket's steering mechanism had not worked properly. It was September before the Atlas finally lifted the capsule into orbit for one trip around the earth. It was a regulation capsule, but there was no life aboard.

It was extremely desirable that the capsule be given a longer test, at least three times around the earth, and that its life support system be tested on something alive. In spite of a growing public interest in getting a man into orbit before the end of 1961, Project Mercury officials went ahead with their plans to attempt an orbital shot with a chimpanzee as a passenger before they sent up an astronaut. So instead of one of the astronauts it was Enos, the astrochimp, who prepared for the next Mercury flight.

Enos was a 37-pound chimp, about the size of a husky four-year-old boy, who had been trained for space flight at a special school at Holloman Air Force Base in New Mexico. He was shot up into orbit on the morning of November 29, 1961. Like the chimpanzee Ham before him, Enos had work to do while he was in space—levers to push in response to a set of signals. His lever-pushing was monitored electronically by scientists on the ground, who were interested in finding out whether prolonged weightlessness would affect his performance.

The astrochimp seemed to be doing all right, but during his second sweep around the earth, things started to go wrong with the capsule. A set of inverters began heating up and so did Enos' cabin. The mechanism for controlling the movement of the capsule was using up the hydrogen-peroxide fuel supply at a rapid rate. The capsule was brought down after it had completed only two orbits.

That complicated maneuver went off without a hitch; the capsule, with Enos inside, was plucked out of the Atlantic south of Bermuda. Enos appeared to have survived his 180-minute trip in fine style. Later, a detailed study of the records revealed that his blood pressure had gone up at the start of the journey and stayed up until he got out of the capsule. Poor Enos had reasons for being upset. He was supposed to get a slight shock when he pushed the incorrect levers. Something went wrong and he was getting a shock even when he pushed the right ones. The trouble with the hydrogen-peroxide fuel-supply system had caused the capsule to rock and Enos had rocked right along with it.

But Enos' difficulties were only temporary. In general, the flight was considered to be a success. So the next Mercury capsule shot into orbit could carry one of the astronauts!

X. OTHER UNITED STATES SPACE PROJECTS

Although Mercury was a high-priority project, it was not the National Aeronautics and Space Administration's only assault on space. Airplanes powered by rockets had been under consideration for high-altitude research before Project Mercury was born. And the X-15 rocket plane was undergoing tests at the same time as the Mercury capsule. Jointly sponsored by NASA, the Air Force, and the Navy, the X-15 program was designed to obtain information on the problems of manned flight at extremely high altitudes.

Headquarters for work with the X-15 is Edwards Air Force Base, located in southern California's Mojave Desert. A 65-square-mile dry lake bed near the base serves as a landing field for the rocket plane. The X-15 lands on skids instead of wheels.

There are other things that are different about the X-15. For wings it has a stubby wedge sticking out from each side of the fuselage. Its tail is a huge vertical fin; its nose is a sharp needle. All of its 50-foot length is covered with a dull black, heat-resistant paint. Its skin is made of Iconel-X, a nickel alloy that can take temperatures up to 1,200 degrees Fahrenheit. Its interior is divided into a small pilot's cockpit, two huge tanks for liquid oxygen and ammonia and, in the rear, a powerful rocket engine. The X-15 is something new, half-airplane and half-missile. It is a missile that can fly back from space.

The X-15 takes off tucked under the wing of an eight-jet B-52. The pilot, wearing a full pressure suit, is already in the X-15's narrow cockpit. He is strapped to an ejection seat and surrounded by switches, buttons, and gauges. Three control sticks are within easy reach. All along the route that the rocket plane will follow as it flies back to Edwards, technicians are waiting with sensitive tracking and monitoring equipment. The X-15 is loaded with instruments to measure, record, and report everything that happens to plane and pilot. This is a research plane. It flies only so that the effects of high altitude and high speed can be studied.

The B-52 jet carries the 16½-ton X-15 nearly 500 miles, climbing until it can climb no higher. Then it turns to point the X-15 toward Edwards. By this time they are at an altitude of 40,000 feet over Wendover Air Force Base near Salt Lake City, Utah. The flight track of the X-15 runs from Wendover back to Edwards Air Force Base.

The X-15 pilot has been working on his pre-launch check list. He now begins the final checks, keeping in touch with the B-52 mother ship by radio. If all of the numerous and complicated systems are working prop-

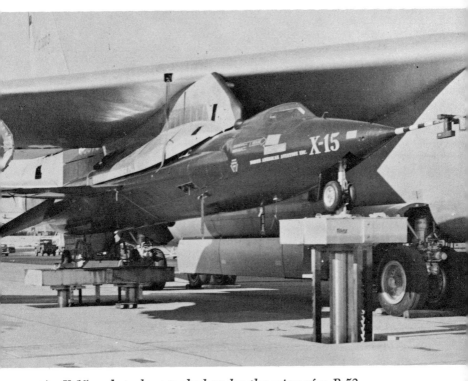

An X-15 rocket plane tucked under the wing of a B-52.

erly, he notifies the B-52 that he is ready for the launch to send him flying off on his own.

The needle-nosed X-15 drops like a rock from under the mother ship's wing, but its rocket engine takes over at once, shooting it skyward. Within seconds the B-52 is far behind and below. As he climbs, the X-15 pilot experiences the same acceleration forces that hit the Mercury astronauts on their take-offs. He too has trained for them in the centrifuge at Johnsville. He can adjust his control sticks with the touch of a finger, and a finger is about all he can move at this point.

He climbs higher and higher, aiming for an altitude 50 miles above the earth. At 40 miles, the X-15's engine, having exhausted its fuel supply, cuts out, but the ship continues to climb. It is carried forward now by the momentum of its great speed, higher and still higher. But acceleration is beginning to fall off. The pilot is no longer squashed back into his seat. The force pushing against him becomes less and less and finally disappears altogether. Now he is weightless.

The X-15, being both spaceship and plane, has two sets of controls—one to use at lower levels and one to use at altitudes where there is not enough atmosphere to support a plane's control surfaces. To maneuver his craft as he floats 50 miles above the earth, the pilot uses the control stick at his left. It activates hydrogen-peroxide jets in the nose and wing tips, a steering process somewhat similar to that used in the Mercury capsule.

Under its own power the X-15 takes off from the mother ship.

When the X-15 has exhausted its climbing momentum and starts back down to earth, it travels at a tremendous speed. The plane is built to go faster than 4,000 miles an hour. As it pushes through the thickening atmosphere, its metal skin begins to heat up. A metal other than Iconel-X would melt. Air conditioning in the cockpit and in his suit keeps the pilot cool.

Down where the air is thicker, the pilot abandons the left control stick and begins to use the ones on his right and in the center. These are aerodynamic controls similar to those found on more conventional planes, and with them he guides the X-15 back to the dry lake bed at Edwards.

There are three teams of pilots assigned to the X-15 project. North American Aviation, its manufacturer, has two test pilots working with the experimental plane. They are Scott Crossfield, the chief engineering pilot, and Alvin White, his back-up. They are responsible for thoroughly testing each of the X-15s to make sure it is airworthy and capable of meeting performance standards.

When North American has finished its test program, two other teams take over. One, composed of Joseph Walker, chief pilot, and Jack McKay and Neil Armstrong, back-ups, makes research flights for the National Aeronautics and Space Administration. Flights for the Air Force are conducted by chief pilot Major Robert White and his back-up, Captain Robert Rushworth. These men are all experienced test pilots who were especially selected and trained to fly the experimental plane.

The centrifuge at Johnsville that was used by the Mercury astronauts was equipped with a replica of the X-15's cockpit so that the X-15 pilots could practice "flying" under conditions similar to those they would experience during high-speed dives, climbs, and turns. They also prepared for actual flight by "flying" X-15 simulators to learn the plane's handling characteristics. Before each flight the pilot assigned to fly the mission makes several simulator runs so that he is thoroughly familiar with all the procedures he must follow while in the air.

The X-15 pilots fly in a specially designed suit which has its own pressurization and air-conditioning systems. Test pilot Scott Crossfield, with the help of the other pilots, took an active part in the development and testing of the suit.

The first flights of the X-15 were glide tests. It was dropped from the B-52 mother ship to glide back to Edwards Air Force Base without using its rocket engine. The first powered flight of the X-15 took place on September 17, 1959, with Scott Crossfield at the controls. He reached a speed of 1,385 miles an hour on that first flight.

That was just the beginning. Plans for the X-15 called for a gradual increase in speed until 4,000 miles an hour was reached and a gradual increase in altitude to 250,000 feet. On May 25, 1961, NASA test pilot

Top. *An X-15 pilot guides the craft to a landing on the dry lake bed at Edwards Air Force Base.* Bottom. *Joseph Walker, Robert White and Scott Crossfield, three X-15 test pilots, confer beside one of the rocket ships.*

Joseph Walker raised the speed to 3,370 miles an hour. A month later Major Robert White pushed it up to 3,603 miles an hour. On October 17, 1961, pilot Walker reached 3,920 miles an hour, and on November 9, 1961, Major White flew the X-15 at a fast 4,070 miles an hour.

While the experimental plane was going faster, it was also going higher. On March 30, 1961, NASA test pilot Walker flew it to a height of 32 miles. Major White raised the X-15's ceiling to 217,000 feet, or about 41 miles, on October 11, 1961. And even that record was broken on May 1, 1962, when Joe Walker flew the X-15 to an altitude of 246,700 feet, or 46.7 miles.

The X-15 program has not been without its mishaps. Its rocket engines have exploded both in the air and during run-up on the ground. Temperature changes of more than 1,000 degrees in less than three minutes have splintered its windshield during flight. Each of the three X-15s has had to be rebuilt or modified as problem areas developed.

There are no plans to build any more X-15s. By the time everything possible has been learned from the X-15 about how pilot and plane function at high speeds and high altitudes, more advanced craft will have been developed to carry the research still farther into space at still faster speeds.

One of the first of these will be the delta-winged Dyna-Soar, so named because its flight is based on the principles of dynamic soaring. A rocket-boosted, hypersonic glider, Dyna-Soar will combine the high speed of a missile with the controlled and accurate flight of a manned airplane just as the X-15 does. But the Dyna-Soar glider will fly much higher and faster. It will be able to attain orbital speed—a fast 18,000 miles an hour. Early Dyna-Soar models will carry a single pilot who will actually "fly" the ship except during the time it is being shot up into orbit by its powerful booster rocket. While he is in orbit, the pilot will be able to make valuable scientific observations because the Dyna-Soar glider will be a research vehicle loaded with many different kinds of instruments. When the time comes to return to earth, he will be able to control his descent to minimize the effects of rapid deceleration and heat build-up as the ship reënters the earth's atmosphere.

He will do this by first pointing the glider's long nose down. As the vehicle descends, it will get hotter and hotter. When the danger point—3,600 degrees Fahrenheit—approaches, the pilot will raise the nose to slow it and cool it off. Then he will point it down again until it gets too hot, then up again to cool off. This skipping back and forth, into and out of the upper fringes of the earth's atmosphere, will slow down the glider. By coming in a little lower each time, the pilot will gradually bring his craft back to earth. He will be able to head for any landing field he chooses. In spite of the great speed attained while in orbit, the Dyna-Soar's landing speed will be in the same range as that of a jet transport.

The Dyna-Soar program is an Air Force project in which NASA is cooperating. The Boeing Airplane Company is building the gliders, which may someday be adapted to carry a two-man crew as a military spacecraft.

In its first flights Dyna-Soar will be dropped from a B-52 mother ship in much the same way as the X-15 is launched. Then will come full orbital flight. It will be boosted into orbit by an advanced booster system being developed by the Martin Company.

The X-15 program has already provided high-altitude flight information that has been of great value to Project Mercury. It is expected that Project Mercury will be completed by the time the first Dyna-Soar craft flies, but information obtained from Dyna-Soar will be used in the development of still more advanced space programs.

XI. THE SOVIET UNION'S SPACE PROGRAM

"The Soviet Union has successfully launched a manned spaceship-satellite into orbit around the earth. Present aboard the spaceship is the pilot cosmonaut, Yuri Gagarin, an air force pilot, 27 years of age!"

This radio announcement, made in Moscow on the morning of April 12, 1961, was greeted with great joy by the Russian people. And as the news of Cosmonaut Gagarin's feat spread, congratulations poured into Moscow from countries all over the world.

President John F. Kennedy, in his congratulatory message, said: "The achievement of the U.S.S.R. of orbiting a man and returning him to the ground is an outstanding technical accomplishment. We congratulate the Soviet scientists and engineers who made this feat possible. The exploration of our solar system is an ambition which we and all mankind share with the Soviet Union and this is an important step toward that goal. Our own Mercury man-in-space program is directed toward the same end."

Indeed it was an important step forward in space exploration. For the first time man had succeeded in freeing himself from the forces that confined him to the planet Earth. He had traveled in space and returned safely, a truly great accomplishment.

Many years of research and experimentation had preceded the successful space flight. Because the Soviet Union releases very little information about its scientific programs, the world may never know all the developments that led up to Cosmonaut Gagarin's flight, but certainly the very best Soviet scientists and engineers worked hard to bring it about.

We have already seen how, in 1957, the Soviet Union had been the first country to successfully launch an unmanned earth satellite and the first to launch a satellite carrying a passenger. That passenger was the dog Laika, who did not survive the trip. The next year two dogs were sent up into space in a special pressurized capsule. They did not travel around the earth, but came down safely after reaching a height of 280 miles. Soon the Soviet Union had several dogs who were veterans of space trips; some of them had been up more than once. The dogs were studied carefully during their journeys. Soviet scientists were gathering information to help them send a man into space.

They were also building and launching spaceships of the type used for Yuri Gagarin's trip. Five of them were sent aloft in the year preceding his successful orbiting of the earth. These spaceships were considerably larger and heavier than the Project Mercury capsules. They weighed over five tons! The powerful boosters developed by Soviet rocket experts could lift a great deal more than the American Atlas.

The Soviet spaceships were described as having two sections. One section was for instruments and the braking mechanism, and the other was a fairly spacious cabin for the pilot, who rode in an ejection seat. By pressing a button he could eject himself and his seat from the cabin. The seat contained the equipment he would need for a forced landing—food, water, radio, a portable oxygen supply, and flares and other devices to attract rescuers.

Inside the cabin the temperature was maintained between 50 and 71.6 degrees Fahrenheit. Air pressure and humidity were regulated at a comfortable level. As in the Mercury capsule, many of the systems were duplicated to insure the cosmonaut's health and safety. Enough supplies were carried to last for ten days.

From his seat the cosmonaut could see the instrument panel with its rotating globe to show him where he was. He could reach the control 'panel, the flight-control stick, an electric clock, and a radio. His cabin had portholes through which he could look during flight.

The spaceship in which Cosmonaut Gagarin traveled was called the *Vostok*, or East. According to Soviet reports, it had been used on two previous orbital flights and recovered undamaged each time.

The cosmonaut was one of a group of pilots who had been preparing for space flight. Their selection and training was in many ways similar to the program for the Mercury astronauts. The Soviet space candidates spent grueling hours in the centrifuge, in heat chambers, in dark soundproof rooms, and in a simulator built to resemble a spaceship's cabin. They too spent a great deal of time studying to prepare themselves for the task ahead.

The man who was chosen to make the first flight, Yuri Gagarin, was a Soviet air force lieutenant who had become interested in aviation at an early age. He was born on March 4, 1934, and spent the years before World War II on a farm with his parents, two sisters, and a brother.

After the war, the family settled in the town of Gzhatsk, where Yuri entered a vocational school to learn to be a molder. His teacher remembers him as a very good pupil, but Yuri was already more interested in aviation than anything else. He took extra courses at a night school and then moved on to a technical school. He also joined an aviation club and learned to fly a Yak trainer. In 1955 he decided to become a military pilot. At the end of a two-year training course, he began his career in the Soviet air force. There he was very busy, but he found time to engage in sports—basketball, skiing, skating, and badminton.

Soon Lieutenant Gagarin heard about the Soviet program for training spacemen. He applied and was accepted as a candidate. And on April 12, 1961, he became the first man to travel in space.

The *Vostok* was launched at 9:07 A.M. Moscow time. Gagarin later reported that the acceleration, noise, and vibration of the launching did not bother him unduly.

Top. *Cosmonaut Yuri Gagarin takes part in a press conference after making the world's first orbital space flight.* Bottom. *Gherman Titov, the second man to orbit the earth, is helped into his space suit.*

When he went into orbit he found that he quickly became used to the sensation of weightlessness. He was able to do his work, eat, drink water, and observe his surroundings.

The pioneer spaceman was impressed with what he saw. The earth had a beautiful blue halo. The sky shaded gradually from blue to violet, and then to black. The stars were very bright against the black sky. Below him he could make out the larger mountains, rivers, and forests, various coastlines and islands. He could see clouds and the shadows they made on the earth.

The *Vostok* made one orbit of the earth. Gagarin reported that he passed into and out of the earth's shadow very quickly. At the end of the trip, when the *Vostok* reëntered the earth's atmosphere, its outside surface became a ball of fire. The cosmonaut confessed later that he was terrified, but inside the spaceship the temperature remained a comfortable 68 degrees Fahrenheit.

The *Vostok* came down in the Russian countryside, reportedly close to the target area. During the 89.1 minutes it had been in orbit around the earth, its altitude had ranged from 110 to 188 miles. From blast-off to landing the trip had taken one hour and forty-eight minutes at an average speed of 17,000 miles an hour.

What was Cosmonaut Gagarin's opinion of space travel? He is reported to have said: "I would like to do a lot of traveling in space. I like it. I would like to go to Venus, to Mars, to do some real flying."

The next cosmonaut to take a space trip was Gherman Titov. On August 6, 1961, he orbited the earth

17½ times. Like Gagarin, Titov was a member of the Russian Air Force and the two men were friends.

Titov was 26. He had grown up in Siberia, the eastern part of the Soviet Union. His father said that Gherman had been an obedient and industrious boy who liked to make things, especially gliders and model airplanes. He liked to read and he did well at his studies. Titov had always wanted to become a pilot. He entered flying school in 1955. Two years later he passed his pilot's examination with a grade of excellent and entered the Soviet Air Force.

The spaceship used by the second cosmonaut was called *Vostok II*. It differed in some respects from *Vostok I*. Many of its systems had been improved, and it carried equipment to televise continuous pictures of the pilot for the information of scientists back on earth.

Vostok II, with Gherman Titov aboard, was launched at nine o'clock in the morning. The cosmonaut carried with him the schedule he was to follow during the 25 hours he was aloft. It told him when to send messages, maneuver his spacecraft, eat, and sleep.

When the time came for his first try at taking over the controls of *Vostok II*, the cosmonaut was worried. Would he be able to steer it? He found to his relief that *Vostok II* managed as easily as a car or plane.

After he had made one circuit of the earth and was flying again over the Soviet Union, Titov—or the Eagle, as he called himself while he was in orbit—radioed: "The flight is progressing successfully. All the equipment of the ship is functioning normally. I am feeling well."

During the third orbit it was time for lunch, three

courses which he ate from tubes. Supper came during the sixth orbit. In between, as he had time, Titov radioed greetings to the peoples of the various continents as he passed over them.

The cosmonaut was scheduled to go to sleep shortly after six o'clock Moscow time, after nine hours in space. He sent the following good-night message to Moscow: "Dear Moscovites, there are no changes in the cabin. The pressure is normal, perfect pressure. Humidity is 70 per cent; temperature is 18 degrees centigrade [64.4 degrees Fahrenheit]. I am perfectly comfortable, perfectly comfortable; I wish you the same. Everything is going well, everything is going marvelously. I beg to wish dear Moscovites good night. I am turning in now. You do as you please, but I am turning in."

Cosmonaut Titov slept so well that he woke up 37 minutes late according to his timetable. *Vostok II* had been making one trip around the earth every 88.6 minutes during the eight hours that he slept. His journey was nearing its end.

After *Vostok II* had traveled around the earth 17 times, the automatic reëntry system went into operation as scheduled. The spaceship left its orbit and began to descend. Like Cosmonaut Gagarin before him, Titov saw the outside of his cabin turn into a ball of fire. Inside, the temperature went no higher than 71.6 degrees Fahrenheit.

As *Vostok II* neared the target area, Titov decided to eject himself from the cabin and come down by parachute instead of remaining with the spaceship as Gagarin had done. He landed on one side of some railroad tracks; *Vostok II* landed on the other. It was 10:18 A.M., Moscow time; Cosmonaut Titov had been gone 25 hours and 18 minutes. He had covered a distance approximately equal to a trip to the moon and back.

Like their counterparts in the United States, Soviet scientists were interested in finding out how prolonged weightlessness would affect a space traveler. Titov's flight told them some of the things they wanted to know. During most of the time he was in orbit, the cosmonaut was mildly "seasick." He was uncomfortable, but able to continue working. His nausea grew worse up to the time he went to sleep and was especially bad whenever he moved his head quickly. He felt better after he had slept, but he didn't recover completely until *Vostok* II began its descent.

Many years before the space trips of Yuri Gagarin and Gherman Titov, Konstantin Ziolkovsky, the man the Russians honor as the "Father of Space Travel," had written: "Man will not remain bound to the earth forever. Step by step he will conquer the space around the sun."

Cosmonauts Gagarin and Titov proved that the prophecy was a true one. Although Soviet scientists made no immediate announcement of plans for future space flights, undoubtedly they were already looking ahead to still longer orbital trips and to the exploration of the moon. Only a truly monster rocket, however, could send a manned spaceship to the moon. So in the Soviet Union, as in the United States, there is still much work to do.

XII. COUNTDOWN

On February 20, 1962, American newspaper headlines proclaimed the story everyone had been waiting for: GLENN ORBITS EARTH THREE TIMES SAFELY. After 1,160 days of hard, painstaking effort, the men of Project Mercury had achieved their goal.

There had been some disheartening setbacks during those 1,160 days, but none were more frustrating than the ones that occurred right at the end. The flight that finally proved to be so successful on February 20 had been postponed no less than ten times!

After the astrochimp Enos completed his two orbits of the earth on November 29, 1961, manned flight around the earth was next on the Project Mercury schedule. Before Enos, an unmanned capsule had made a successful orbit. In both firings the capsule and the Atlas booster had performed well. There was nothing more that could be learned until a man was placed in orbit.

The man chosen to make the all-important trip was— Lieutenant Colonel John H. Glenn, Jr., at 40 the oldest of the seven astronauts. His alternate, the astronaut who would go if Glenn should become ill, was Lieutenant Commander Malcolm Scott Carpenter. The date was tentatively set for some time before the end of the year. It was hoped that, like the Soviet Union, the United States would be able to orbit a man in 1961.

The length of time spent in preparation between the Mercury launchings had averaged about six weeks. After Enos' flight, workers at Cape Canaveral thought that by working extra hours they could be ready in less time. But there was too much to do and too much at stake to take chances on hasty work. The date was finally set for January 16, 1962. And even that proved to be too soon.

During the pre-flight check a defect was found in the capsule's air-conditioning system; it meant a week's delay. The repairs couldn't be completed in a week—another delay. Then there was trouble with the emergency oxygen supply to the capsule's cabin and the astronaut's pressure suit. The date of the launching had to be set back again—to January 27.

This time the preliminary checks indicated that both the Atlas and the capsule were ready to go. Astronaut Glenn, who had been training daily for the flight, was also ready. It looked as if January 27 might be the big day.

The astronaut was up at two in the morning. At 5:15 A.M. he climbed into the space capsule. The moon was shining and everything still looked good for the launching.

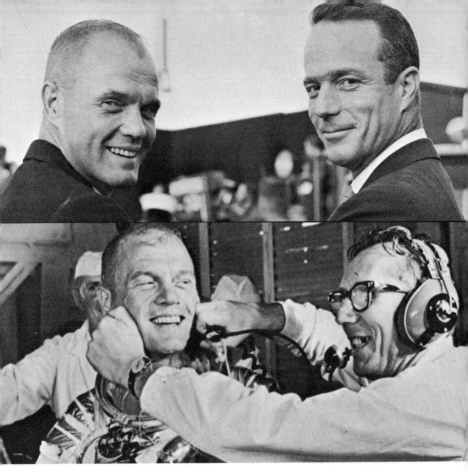

Top. *Astronaut John Glenn (left) was selected to make the first American orbital space flight around the earth, with Scott Carpenter (right) as alternate.* Bottom. *Glenn gets a friendly chuck on the cheek from technician Guenter Wendt after the January 27 flight is postponed.*

At 9:10 A.M. the flight was called off. Several minor technical difficulties had held up the countdown. While technicians worked to correct them, an unexpected cloud cover rolled in over Cape Canaveral. It was thick and it showed no signs of lifting. Project Mercury officials would not be able to follow the Atlas as it lifted off the pad. The safety of the astronaut depended on optical as well as electronic tracking.

"Well, there'll be another day," said the weary Colonel Glenn as he left the launching pad after four hours in the capsule.

As it turned out, there were to be several more days. Fuel had leaked into an insulated bulkhead of the Atlas missile. The insulation had to be replaced. And then the weather caused more delays. Like Astronauts Shepard and Grissom before him, Glenn would land in the Atlantic, and weather is usually bad in the mid-Atlantic during February. A series of storms moved across the area. The waiting recovery ships pitched and rolled in strong winds and waves 20 feet high. A capsule landing in such seas was apt to be lost.

The storms continued to move in; Cape Canaveral and the whole country continued to wait. The Atlas booster and the capsule stood on Pad 14 ready to go. Astronaut Glenn went over his flight procedures again and again. Project Mercury was close to achieving its goal. Everything depended on the weather.

During the frustrating days of waiting there were some who said Project Mercury was being too cautious; the officials were too insistent that everything be super-safe. "All progress involves some risk," they said. "Lindbergh would never have crossed the Atlantic if he had been flying for Project Mercury."

But Mercury officials refused to take any chances. Their job was to send a man into space and into orbit, and then *bring him safely back to earth.* They wanted to learn if man could carry out useful activities while traveling in space. No activity could be called useful if the man didn't come back safely.

There was another reason why Project Mercury was proceeding cautiously. None of its activities were being kept secret. The whole world could watch, and was watching, what happened at Cape Canaveral. The Soviet Union had already sent two men into orbit around the earth. Now it was the turn of the United States. Failure would mean a serious loss of prestige.

The sky was covered with clouds when John Glenn was awakened at 2:20 on the morning of February 20, 1962. Although the weather didn't look encouraging, out at the launch area the final countdown had begun at 11:30 P.M. Breakfast was at 2:45 A.M.—orange juice, scrambled eggs, steak, and toast. The same menu had been prepared for Astronauts Shepard and Grissom, and for Glenn himself, on January 27.

The physical examination, which started at three, lasted an hour. In spite of the weary days of waiting, the astronaut was in excellent shape. And so were the Atlas and the capsule. The countdown was proceeding without a hitch.

At 4:00 A.M. the count was stopped at T minus 120 minutes. This was a planned hold to give the technicians some extra time if they needed it. So far everything was right on schedule. By 4:30 Astronaut Glenn was getting into his 20-pound space suit. Pressure tests to make sure the suit would hold oxygen were next.

At five o'clock he was ready to leave Hangar S for the launching area. It was still cloudy. Astronaut Carpenter and the flight surgeon rode to Pad 14 with Glenn. Pad 14 was a blaze of lights. Shortly after the astronauts arrived, the planned hold was extended for 45 minutes. Trouble had been discovered in the guidance system of the Atlas booster.

At six o'clock Glenn left the van that had brought him from Hangar S. Crewmen working in the launching area could see him smile behind his space visor as he walked briskly to the elevator. There had been some breaks in the clouds, but they had closed in again. Above the capsule, which had been named Friendship 7, the sky was black and forbidding.

The countdown was resumed at 6:26—T minus 120. The astronaut was in the capsule and the hatch was closed, but he couldn't be sealed in. There was a broken bolt on the hatch cover. The bolt had to be replaced. It was now 7:25—T minus 60 and holding. The sky was still covered with clouds.

And so it went with the hands of the clock getting ever closer to nine. There was growing concern about the time. Unless Friendship 7 could be launched before

Top. *Astronaut Glenn, accompanied by flight surgeon William Douglas, leaves Hangar S on the morning of February 20, 1962.* Bottom. *Mercury-Atlas 6 zooms into the air, launching Glenn on the first United States orbital flight.*

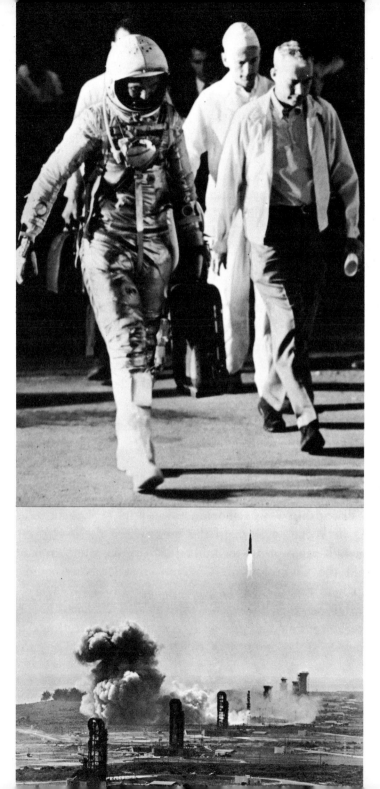

9:30 or 9:45, its orbits would have to be reduced to two or even to one. For a safe recovery there had to be an ample margin of daylight left in the Atlantic landing area.

At 9:30 A.M. the count had reached T minus 15 minutes. Both the astronaut in the capsule and the Mercury officials monitoring the launching were reporting all systems "Go." The clouds that had hung over the Cape were gone. A beautiful sun was shining, and a feeling of optimism had replaced the earlier gloom.

After just one more short delay, the count was resumed for the last time at 9:42. When the clock moved past 9:46, the count was in seconds: nine, eight, seven, six, five, four, three, two, one, zero!

Fire and smoke appeared under the tail of the Atlas. The 130-ton rocket rose slowly from the launching pad trailing a bright, white-yellow flame. With a roar it went streaking skyward followed by a thin white vapor trail. Within seconds it was gone.

From his capsule perched on top of the speeding Atlas, Astronaut Glenn reported: "Lift off, the clock is operating, we're under way."

Friendship 7 was moving toward its orbital altitude. As he rocketed through the area where there was still enough atmosphere to buffet the capsule, the astronaut told the Control Center: "Some vibration area coming up here now."

But he was having no trouble. All his instruments were working and he was reporting their readings to the Control Center in a calm, steady voice. The man

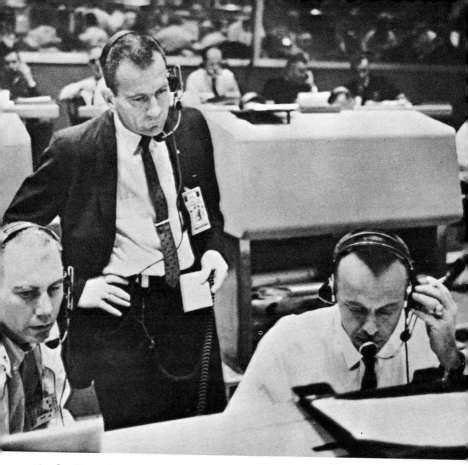

At the Cape Canaveral Control Center, Flight Surgeon William Douglas (left) and astronauts Donald Slayton (center) and Alan Shepard monitor Glenn's historic flight.

who was receiving his messages was Alan Shepard, the astronaut whose ride in the capsule Freedom 7 had made him the United States' first spaceman.

From the moment of launching the men in the Control Center had been greatly concerned with the flight path of the Atlas. Any variation from the planned direction would send the capsule into an orbit over areas where it could not be tracked and where it would be difficult to recover after landing. Likewise, the capsule's speed had to be just right. If it didn't reach a speed close to 17,500 miles an hour at the proper point, it wouldn't go into orbit at all and would have to be brought down at once. Too much speed, on the other hand, would result in an unplanned orbit that might expose the astronaut to dangerous radiation. And when the capsule came down, it might be out of reach of the recovery forces.

The two booster engines of the Atlas had exhausted their fuel two minutes after the launching, leaving the 60,000-pound thrust sustainer engine to lift the capsule into orbit. After five minutes of flight it, too, burned out, and Friendship 7 went into orbit at 17,545 miles an hour.

Computers at the Goddard Space Flight Center at Greenbelt, Maryland, had been electronically monitoring the Atlas since it was one-half of one inch off the launching pad. Within two-and-a-half seconds after the capsule went into orbit, information on its speed, elevation, and direction had been transmitted to Goddard, run through the computers there, and the results sent to the Cape. It was a good orbit!

From the Mercury Control Center Alan Shepard relayed the happy news to Glenn in Friendship 7. "You have a go. At least seven orbits."

That meant that the orbit attained by Friendship 7 was good enough to carry it seven times around the earth. The plan, however, called for it to come down after three trips.

Upon going into orbit, Friendship 7 had turned around so that its blunt end was forward. This enabled Glenn to look back toward Cape Canaveral. Like Gagarin, Titov, Shepard, and Grissom—all of whom had traveled in space before him—the astronaut was greatly impressed with what he saw below him. There was a big cloud pattern stretching all the way to Florida. "Oh, that view is tremendous!" he exclaimed.

XIII. THREE TIMES AROUND THE EARTH

As Friendship 7 sped across the Atlantic, the Mercury tracking network stood ready to follow its progress with radio and radar. Each one of the 18 stations scattered around the globe was in constant communication with the Goddard Space Flight Center and with the Mercury Control Center at Cape Canaveral. The tracking stations were located so that the astronaut would be within range of one of them for almost his entire journey.

Each time it circled the earth, Friendship 7 would follow a slightly different path due to the earth's rotation. Because the overall orbit pattern had been planned with the possibility of a forced landing in mind, the capsule was routed over the United States and over water as much as possible. Its path swung back and forth across the equator, ranging from about 32 degrees north of it to 32 degrees south.

From the space craft came a constant stream of radioed reports on the condition of the astronaut and his capsule. The station at Bermuda began receiving these reports three minutes after the launching. Then Friendship 7 passed within range of a tracking ship in the

Atlantic and the stations located at Grand Canary off the coast of Africa and at Kano in Nigeria. To the men at Grand Canary Astronaut Glenn radioed: "I am very comfortable. All systems are O.K."

By 10:28 he had eaten two tubes of food, one meat and the other fruit, and some malted-milk tablets. Having left Africa behind him, he was in contact with the tracking ship in the Indian Ocean as he headed toward Australia.

When he crossed the East African coast, Glenn entered the night of February 20. It was still night when he reached Australia. The citizens of Perth and Rockingham, in the western part of that country, had turned on all their lights in the hope that the spaceman would be able to see them. To Astronaut Gordon Cooper, who was the capsule communicator at the tracking station at Muchea, Australia, John Glenn reported that he saw some very bright lights, and he added, "Thank everyone for turning them on, will you?"

Another day dawned as he traveled across the Pacific. Speaking of his first "day" in space, Colonel Glenn said: "That was sure a short day. That was about the shortest day I've ever run into!"

With the coming of daylight, the astronaut saw that his space craft was surrounded by thousands of luminous particles ranging in size from the head of a pin to three-eighths of an inch. They seemed to be moving at the same speed as the capsule. He didn't know what they were, but they caused him no difficulty. At this point he was experiencing no difficulties of any kind.

As he approached the coast of Mexico, however, he

began to have trouble with the capsule's automatic attitude-control system. This was supposed to keep the blunt end of the capsule pointing upward and forward. Instead it was swinging to the right so that the capsule was moving sideways through space. The astronaut reported that he had started to "fly-by-wire," meaning that he was keeping the space craft in a proper position by manual control.

Still flying-by-wire as he passed over Cape Canaveral, but having no trouble controlling the capsule, Astronaut Glenn reported to Alan Shepard in the Control Center on what he thought had gone wrong. From the Control Center came the advice: "Recommend you remain fly-by-wire."

Friendship 7's first orbit of the earth was completed at 11:21 A.M.; it had taken 88 minutes and 29 seconds. Astronaut Glenn was in excellent condition. His electrocardiogram, respiration rate, and blood pressure were all normal. When asked if he had experienced any of the dizziness and nausea that had bothered Cosmonaut Titov, he had answered: "No symptoms whatsoever. I feel fine."

At 11:26 A.M. the astronaut was again in contact with the Bermuda tracking stations as he started around the earth for a second time. High above the Atlantic the sun was shining brightly. He told the trackers in the Canary Islands: "The sun coming through the window is very, very warm where it hits the suit. I get quite a bit of heat from it."

Top. *From the tracking station at Muchea, Australia, Astronaut Gordon Cooper (in black shirt) and command team follow Glenn's flight.* Bottom. *A picture of the west coast of Mexico taken from an orbiting Mercury spaceship.*

On he flew, across Africa and into his second night over the Eastern Hemisphere. At 12:45 P.M. Glenn was approaching the west coast of the United States for the second time. From Hawaii he had sent word that he was ready to go for another orbit. To Astronaut Wally Schirra at the Point Arguello, California, tracking station, he reported: "I feel real good, Wally. No problems at all."

This was a time of decision for the men at the Mercury Control Center at Cape Canaveral. Should Friendship 7 be brought down because of the trouble with the attitude-control system, or should it be allowed to go on for three orbits? The astronaut seemed to be having no trouble with his manual control of the capsule. The decision was made: Three orbits!

This time, as Friendship 7 flashed over Florida, Glenn worked out some landing details with Alan Shepard at Mercury Control. Crossing the Atlantic for the third time, he got a wide view of the area in which he would be coming down. "It looks very good down that way," he reported. "It looks like we'll have no problems on recovery."

The astronaut's optimistic statement brought little cheer to Mercury Flight Director Christopher Columbus Kraft at the Control Center. Since the end of the first orbit the trackers on the ground had been receiving a signal that indicated the capsule's heat shield was loose. This was a development that caused considerable alarm. Unless the heat shield was in place when Friendship 7 reëntered the atmosphere, there was little chance that the astronaut would survive the trip back to earth.

Kraft called in Kenneth Kleinknecht, the newly named Mercury Project Manager, and Bill Bland, a Mercury expert. While they were trying to decide what to do, Astronaut Alan Shepard and Systems Monitor Don Arabian began going over blueprints and wiring diagrams to see if they could spot something that could have gone wrong with the capsule's circuitry. They all felt that the signal was a false one, but they couldn't be sure.

The capsule moved on in its third orbit and into night for the third time in four hours. As it passed over Hawaii for the last time, a special check was made on the heat shield. It seemed to be all right; evidently the signal had been erroneous. After hurried, and worried, consultations the Mercury controllers on the ground advised Astronaut Glenn not to jettison his retro-rockets after they fired. Their straps would help hold the heat shield in case it was loose. Spent retro-rockets had never been retained before. They might give some trouble on the way down, but not nearly so much trouble as a loose heat shield.

The astronaut was ready to begin his descent from space. He had secured all his loose equipment and checked his control systems. At 2:20, as he approached the California coast, the retro-rocket firing began—three braking rockets to slow the capsule and start it on its downward journey. As they fired against the direction of the space craft, the astronaut received quite a

While Astronaut Glenn was traveling at a speed of 17,500 miles an hour, an automatic motion picture camera installed in the capsule took this picture.

jolt. "I feel like I'm going back to Hawaii," he told Walter Schirra at Point Arguello.

"You don't want to do that. You want to go to the east coast," was the answer.

And that, of course, was exactly the direction in which Glenn was headed, loosing altitude steadily as his speed decreased. Off Florida's east coast the capsule reëntered the earth's atmosphere. The astronaut was in contact with the Cape Canaveral Control Center, and Alan Shepard was giving him landing instructions. Then, as the capsule passed through the ionosphere— the outer regions of the earth's atmosphere—contact was lost for three long minutes. In that area the radio frequencies they were using couldn't get to, or out of, the capsule.

Meanwhile Astronaut Glenn was having what he described later as a "rather spectacular reëntry." The capsule was still carrying the spent retro-rockets. There was a slight bump, and he thought, "There goes the rocket packet." (He had expected the heat of reëntry to burn it off.) Then he saw some "fire balls"—bright, burning chunks of metal—fly past his window. If the rocket packet was already gone, the only thing left to go was the heat shield. If the heat shield was tearing up it meant, as he said later, "a bad day all the way around."

Actually it was the rocket package burning; he hadn't lost the heat shield after all. The heat turned the capsule to a bright orange. With the outside temperature at 3,000 degrees Fahrenheit, Glenn felt like a man inside a glowing fire. When voice communication was reëstablished, his message was: "Boy, that was a real fireball!"

The capsule's small drogue parachute opened on schedule at 21,000 feet, followed by the larger main chute. ". . . the prettiest little old sight you ever saw in your life," said the astronaut.

He splashed into the sea 166 miles east of Grand Turk Island at 2:43 P.M., 4 hours and 56 minutes and 81,000 miles after the launching at Cape Canaveral. His three orbits had taken him from 98.9 to 162.5 miles above the earth.

The astronaut had already been in contact with the destroyer *Noa* of the recovery fleet. Now from the *Noa*, about six miles away, came the message: "Seven, understand your condition is excellent." Then, as the destroyer came closer to the bobbing spacecraft came the further advice: "We expect to pick you up shortly."

Twenty-one minutes after the landing, a slightly scorched Friendship 7 with Glenn inside was hoisted aboard the *Noa*. "My condition is excellent," he assured the waiting world.

The next day, after the astronaut had been taken to Grand Turk Island in the Bahamas for an exhaustive post-flight examination, a team of doctors and technicians confirmed that he was indeed in excellent physical condition. They were unable to detect any ill effects from his 4 hours and 45 minutes of weightless flight or from the 8 g's he had encountered as he returned to earth.

Top. *Glenn stands on the deck of the destroyer Noa.* Bottom. *During the post-flight debriefing aboard the USS Randolph, Glenn enjoys a cup of coffee.*

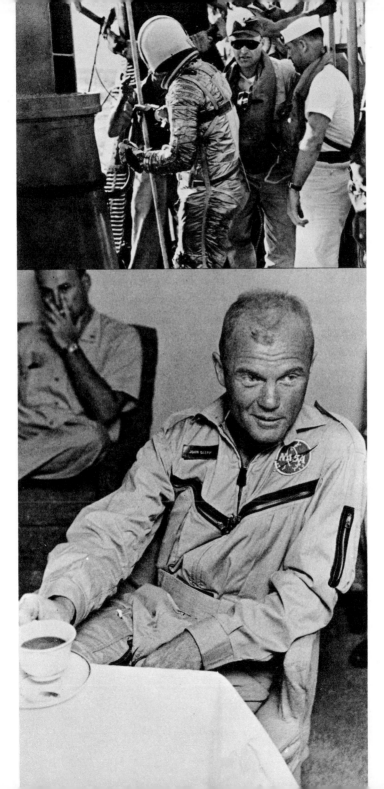

Astronaut Glenn had been advised to avoid rapid movements of his head and body while he was weightless, but he soon found this precaution unnecessary. In fact he tried out various head movements to see if certain movements or combinations of movements would produce distortion or nausea. The results were negative. He felt no ill effects whatsoever. He was able to manipulate the capsule's switches with ease, and when he ate he swallowed his food without difficulty.

At a news conference Glenn had this advice to offer hungry spacemen of the future: "I think the only restriction probably to food will be that it not be of a particularly crumbly nature like crumbly cookies that have little particles to them that might break off and you wouldn't be able to get these back unless you had a butterfly net of some kind. As long as the food is solid you can hold on to it and get it into your mouth and from that point on there appears to be no problem."

The astronaut was surprised at the speed with which he became used to weightlessness. He had been weightless only 30 or 45 minutes when he was casually parking things in mid-air. He reported this incident: "I was using a hand-held camera. Another system needed attention, so it seemed quite natural to let go of the camera, take care of another chore in the space craft, then reach out, grasp the camera and go back about my business."

A study of the medical data relayed from Friendship 7 during its flight indicated that the astronaut functioned

Congressmen of both Houses listen closely as Astronaut John H. Glenn, Jr., describes his orbital flight.

normally at all times. In fact he had been able to do more than had been planned for him. The difficulties with the capsule's attitude-control system had made him a full-time pilot in space.

In summing up the flight, Project Mercury's operations director, Walter C. Williams, said: "It was 100 per cent successful." But Mercury officials made it clear that it would not have been such a success if Astronaut Glenn had not been such a skillful space pilot. He had saved the mission.

There could no longer be any doubt about the wisdom and need of sending men into space. The astronaut had used skilled judgment in overcoming the difficulties he encountered. No instrument could do that, and no instrument could have reported as accurately on the unexpected, such as the luminous particles that appeared around the capsule at sunrise.

As a further check on the capabilities of man in space, Project Mercury sent a second astronaut, Scott Carpenter, on a three-orbit flight on May 24, 1962. Project Mercury officials felt that the first flight had not fully tested the capsule or the ground-control system. Also, they wished to test certain changes made in the capsule as a result of Glenn's flight.

Carpenter's space ship was named Aurora 7, and his flight was as successful as Glenn's. It proved to have a more suspenseful ending, however, for Aurora 7 overshot the designated landing area by more than 250 miles. For nearly an hour the watching nation waited impatiently, wondering if he was still alive. A Navy patrol plane

To honor America's orbiting hero, New York City staged a ticker-tape parade second only to Charles Lindbergh's.

finally spotted the astronaut floating on a rubber raft near the capsule. A team of para-rescuemen landed near him with a larger raft, and soon helicopters picked up the men and carried them to the carrier *Intrepid*.

After Carpenter's success, the National Aeronautics and Space Administration talked of progressing to flights of six, seven and a half and eighteen orbits. Cosmonaut Titov suffered from dizziness and nausea when he was in orbit for 25 hours. Scientists wanted to know if this would happen to all men who were weightless that long.

Although there was still much to be learned about space flight, the successful orbiting of astronauts John Glenn and Scott Carpenter had made an important contribution to our understanding of what man could do in space. Project Mercury was achieving its goal.

Astronaut Scott Carpenter, dressed for his trip in Aurora 7, leaves the special van which carried him from the hangar to the launch area.

XIV. AFTER PROJECT MERCURY

It is a summer night in the late 1960s. The moon has just risen and hangs like a huge orange ball above the eastern horizon. The night is a clear one; the bumps and depressions that make up the features of the "man in the moon" are clearly visible. From the earth they look the same as they have always looked. But everything is not the same! In that lunar region which astronomers have named Mare Imbrium, the right eye of the "man in the moon," a rocket ship carrying three men has landed. The exploration of the moon has begun!

Perhaps that momentous landing will take place as early as 1967. There is a great deal to be done first, and many problems will have to be solved. But the scientists of the National Aeronautics and Space Administration are already hard at work. In fact they began even before Project Mercury had been brought to a successful conclusion. Project Apollo is the name that has been given to the United States program for lunar exploration—a series of three-man space flights that will culminate in a landing on the moon. Between it and Project

Mercury will come Project Gemini—Gemini means twins —several flights that have been planned for a two-seater spaceship to prepare the way for the trip to the moon.

The Gemini spaceship will be similar in design to the Mercury capsule but it will be about a fifth again as large to make room for a second astronaut. Twelve of the Gemini spaceships have been ordered from the Mc-Donnell Aircraft Corporation, the firm that built the Mercury capsule. They will be able to carry enough equipment to spend a week or more in a 150-mile-high orbit around the earth. A modified Titan II rocket will do the boosting.

The seven Mercury astronauts will be the ones to fly the Gemini missions. Their knowledge and experience will be needed for the delicate maneuvers that are planned for Gemini. After the new spaceship has been tested, its two-man crew will attempt to rendezvous with an unmanned Agena space craft while in orbit. If they can guide their Gemini spaceship alongside the orbiting Agena, the next step will be an attempt to hook the two vehicles together. They will have to be brought together gently for there would be no way to repair smashups. And the link-up would have to be automatic. It will be some time before astronauts can work outside their ships while in space. This difficult maneuver, which is known as docking, plays an important part in plans for Project Apollo.

There are two ways of getting a spaceship to the moon. One way is to develop a rocket big enough to supply the millions of pounds of thrust needed for the

238,900-mile journey. The rocket being considered for the job is the Nova, a giant 360 feet high and 50 feet in diameter. It will take a long time to perfect the Nova and to build facilities to test and launch it. (These facilities will also have to be giant size.)

Docking is the other method of getting to the moon. Because the approach would be in two stages, smaller boosters could be used. If Project Gemini produces a successful technique for docking two space vehicles in orbit, we might get to the moon as much as two years sooner than if we waited for the big Nova rocket.

If the docking method is used, two Saturn rockets will be launched 90 minutes apart. (The Saturn is another product of Wernher von Braun and his missile team.) The first Saturn will lift a fully loaded third rocket into a carefully planned orbit. The second Saturn will carry the Apollo spaceship and its crew of three into the same orbit. While in orbit the two sections will rendezvous and dock. Then the rocket lifted into space by the first Saturn will take over and supply the thrust to lift the Apollo spaceship the rest of the way to the moon.

Before Project Apollo gets that far, there will have been a series of less complicated flights to prepare the way. The Ranger program which began in 1961 is the first of these. Unmanned Ranger space craft will make "hard," or crash, landings on the moon. Just before each landing, a TV camera will take pictures of the moon's surface and transmit them back to earth. Ranger will also measure radiation near the moon and disturbances on its surface.

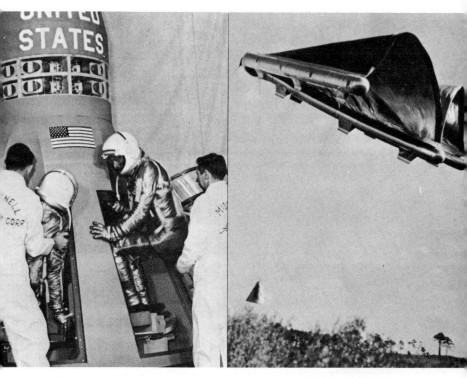

Left. Two engineers get into a full-scale model of Gemini, the two-man space craft being developed by McDonnell Aircraft. Right. Early model of the "Rogallo Wing," to be deployed like a parachute in gliding the Gemini space capsule to dry land. It is expected that a more advanced version will be folded inside the space craft for use in the later Project Gemini flights.

The first Saturn C-1 launch vehicle to come off the assembly line.

Next will come Surveyor, another unmanned-space-craft program. It will make "soft" landings on the moon by using braking rockets for a slow descent. Surveyor space craft will carry a variety of instruments for investigating conditions on the moon. The information collected will help determine the best landing place for a manned spaceship. There may be one more program, Prospector, to gather more detailed information about the surface of the moon prior to an expedition by a manned Apollo spaceship.

Sometime in 1965 the men who will go to the moon may begin their practice flights. Boosted by a "little" Saturn rocket, the three-man crews will first spend a week orbiting the earth in the Apollo spaceship. Perhaps during the next year a more powerful version of the Saturn will be ready to send them to the moon. They will travel around it and return to the earth. The trip is expected to take about a week. If all goes well, this trip may be followed by the first landing on the moon.

The Apollo spaceship is already under development on the drawing boards and in the shops of North American Aviation. It will be built in sections that can be varied for different missions. The three-man crews will live and work in the command section at the front. Other sections will carry supplies and equipment of various kinds.

Who will go to the moon? Not the Mercury astronauts, for they will be too old. They will be serving as instructors, giving a new group of astronauts the benefit of their knowledge and experience.

Full-scale model of a three-man Apollo space capsule. One astronaut is in his couch flying the craft, another is sleeping, and the third is taking a navigational bearing.

The new men will be of the same high caliber as the original seven. In fact the requirements may become even more rigorous. New techniques and equipment will make future astronauts more active participants in space travel. They will have to endure the hostile conditions of space for longer periods of time. While working on the moon, they will have to make accurate observations in a number of specialized fields. The National Aeronautics and Space Administration is confident it will find the best men to go to the moon just as it found the best men for the pioneering Mercury trips into space.

And after the moon will come the planets.

But all future space exploration carried out by the United States will be indebted to the solid achievements of Project Mercury. The successful orbiting of Astronaut John Glenn in Friendship 7 marked the end of the beginning of American space efforts.

Selected List of Some Significant Satellites and Space Probes

Name	Launch Date

Sputnik 1 (USSR) October 4, 1957
The first artificial satellite of the earth

Sputnik 2 (USSR) November 3, 1957
Carried first living passenger, the dog Laika, into orbit

Explorer 1 (USA) January 31, 1958
Discovered inner Van Allen radiation belt

Vanguard 1 (USA) March 17, 1958
Contained radio powered by solar cells; obtained valuable information on size and shape of earth

Sputnik 3 (USSR) May 15, 1958
Carried 2,925 pounds of scientific instruments

Explorer 4 (USA) July 26, 1958
Obtained valuable information about radiation levels

Pioneer 1 (USA) October 11, 1958
Determined presence of interplanetary magnetic field; reached an altitude of 70,700 miles

Project Score (USA) December 18, 1958
First radio repeater satellite; carried record of President Eisenhower's voice

Lunik 1 (USSR) January 2, 1959
First artificial planet of solar system

Discoverer 1 (USA) February 28, 1959
First satellite to go into a polar orbit

Pioneer 4 (USA) March 3, 1959
Went into orbit around the sun

Explorer 6 (USA) August 7, 1959
Took first crude television pictures of earth

Lunik 2 (USSR) September 12, 1959
First probe to hit the moon (September 13, 1959)

Lunik 3 (USSR) October 4, 1959
Took first photographs of hidden side of the moon and transmitted them to the earth

Name   *Launch Date*

Pioneer 5 (USA)   March 11, 1960
 Went into solar orbit; sent radio signals from more than 22
 million miles away
Tiros 1 (USA)   April 1, 1960
 First weather satellite; photographed cloud cover
Transit 1B (USA)   April 13, 1960
 First navigational satellite; sent radio signals to aid naviga-
 tion of ships and planes in all weather
Discoverer 14 (USA)   August 18, 1960
 First mid-air recovery of orbiting man-made object
Sputnik 8 (USSR)   February 12, 1961
 First satellite to launch another vehicle from orbit; first at-
 tempt at Venus probe
Vostok 1 (USSR)   April 12, 1961
 First manned space craft to go into orbit and return
Explorer 11 (USA)   April 27, 1961
 First astronomical observatory satellite
Mercury-Redstone 3
     (USA)   May 5, 1961
 First U.S. manned suborbital space flight; Freedom 7
Mercury-Redstone 4
     (USA)   July 21, 1961
 Second U.S. manned suborbital space flight; Liberty Bell 7
Vostock 2 (USSR)   August 6, 1961
 First manned space craft to orbit earth 17 times
Mercury-Atlas 6 (USA)   February 20, 1962
 First U.S. manned space craft to go into orbit; circled earth
 three times

GLOSSARY

Acceleration. The rate of increase in the velocity or speed of a moving object.

Aerodynamics. The study of air as it moves around objects which may be either motionless or in motion themselves.

Afterburner. A device for increasing the thrust of a turbojet engine by injecting and burning fuel in a duct located behind the engine. Sometimes called a *tailpipe burner.*

Atlantic Missile Range. An area in the Atlantic Ocean—extending for 5,000 miles between Cape Canaveral and Ascension Island—over which many U.S. missiles are tested. The range has a series of tracking stations that gather data on the missiles being tested.

Attitude control system. A system that automatically provides control of the position of a rocket or space craft in relation to some reference line or some fixed set of references.

Automatic pilot. A device that automatically steers an airplane or space craft in the desired direction and keeps it at the proper altitude.

Ballistic missile. A missile which is propelled and guided only during the upward part of its flight, after which it follows a path similar to that of an artillery shell as it falls back to earth.

Blockhouse. A structure, usually of reinforced concrete, near the launching pad. It houses the control systems for the launching of a missile, protecting both them and the launching personnel from blast, heat, and possible explosion during a launching.

Booster. A missile's first stage, supplying the initial thrust needed for launching. It usually operates for a very short time. The term is sometimes used to describe the entire rocket system that propels an artificial satellite or space craft into orbit.

Bulkhead. A wall or partition built across an airplane fuselage or space craft to strengthen it or divide it into sections.

Capsule communicator. The man who is in direct radio contact with the astronaut during space flight. The capsule communicator relays information to the astronaut and answers the astronaut's questions.

Centrifuge. A machine which utilizes centrifugal force (the force tending to pull a body away from the center around which it is revolving) to create an approximation of high gravitational forces.

Contour couch. A form-fitting couch made of two layers of fiber glass with foam material between the layers. It is individually fitted to the astronaut to provide him with support during the periods of high acceleration in space flight.

Cosmic rays. Rays consisting of electrically charged particles of high penetrating power. They originate in outer space.

Deceleration. Moving with decreasing speed.

Drogue parachute. A type of parachute used to slow down a space craft as it returns to earth.

Ejection seat. A seat designed to be catapulted or hurled, with its occupant, from an airplane or space craft—usually by an explosive force of some kind.

Fly-by-wire. A system of controlling a space craft in which the astronaut's manual control stick is electronically connected to the jet valves of the automatic system.

Gantry. A frame structure similar to a scaffold used for assembling and servicing large rockets. It allows workmen to reach all parts of the rocket and can be moved back and forth on rails as it is needed.

G-force. Used as a unit of measurement for bodies undergoing acceleration. One g equals the earth's normal gravitational pull. For each g of acceleration a man's body is subjected to a force that is a multiple of his weight. For instance, under a force of 3 g's a 200-pound man will be subjected to a force of 600 pounds.

Gravity. The mutual attraction that masses of matter have for each other. Gravity or gravitation is the force that holds the universe together. *Also.* The attraction of the earth for objects near its surface.

Guidance system. The sensing devices, computers, and other apparatus needed to develop data on the altitude and path of a missile and to translate that data into commands to the missile's automatic control system.

Guided missile. A missile which can be directed throughout its flight either by signals from the ground or by directions originating in the missile itself.

Hard landing. An uncontrolled landing in which the approach velocity is greater than 500 feet per second.

Hypersonic. Capable of moving at a speed five or more times that of sound.

Inverter. A device for changing direct (D-C) current into alternating (A-C) current.

Ionosphere. A section of the earth's atmosphere which extends from about 50 miles above the earth's surface to a height of 250 or more miles. The ionosphere is so named because it is composed of *ions*, or electrified atoms or molecules.

Life support system. The mechanisms in the space capsule that supply the oxygen necessary to keep the astronaut alive, maintain the proper pressure inside the cabin or in the astronaut's suit, remove carbon dioxide and excess water from the capsule's atmosphere, and regulate the temperature of both the astronaut and the cabin.

Liquid fuel. A rocket fuel consisting of chemicals in the liquid state.

Meteor. A body of solid material which originates in space and becomes incandescent with heat when it enters the earth's atmosphere.

Nose cone. The section at the forward end of a rocket or missile which carries scientific instruments, test animals or, in the case of military missiles, explosives.

Orbit. The path taken by a body or space vehicle in its flight around another object.

Override. To use a manually operated control to supplant or neutralize the operation of an automatic control.

Periscope. An optical instrument consisting of a tube, lenses, and mirrors so arranged that a person at one end of the tube sees what is reflected in the mirror at the other end.

Pressure chamber. A chamber within which air pressure, temperature, etc. can be adjusted to simulate conditions at different altitudes. (Sometimes called an altitude chamber.)

Pressurize. To introduce and maintain inside a spaceship, aircraft cabin, or special suit a pressure higher than that which exists on the outside.

Retro-rocket. A rocket fired to produce a thrust against the forward motion of a space craft, thereby decreasing its speed.

Satellite. Any body, man-made or natural, that revolves around a larger body.

Simulator. A training device that reproduces certain conditions of actual flight.

Soft landing. A landing on the moon or other celestial body at a speed slow enough (less than 500 feet per second) to preserve the space vehicle from damage.

Solid fuel. A nonliquid rocket fuel which uses dry chemicals.

Sounding rocket. A research rocket equipped with instruments for obtaining data on the upper atmosphere.

Suborbital flight. Space flight at a speed insufficient to carry the space craft into orbit.

Supersonic. Having a speed greater than sound.

Sustainer engine. The engine that propels a rocket after the engine or engines that supplied the initial thrust have cut off.

Telemetering. A system of recording space or missile data by radioing an instrument reading from a rocket or space vehicle to a recording machine on the ground.

Thrust. The propelling force developed by a rocket engine, usually measured in pounds or tons.

Weightlessness. A condition that exists when the outward pull of centrifugal force equals and therefore cancels out the downward pull of gravity.

Wind tunnel. A tubelike structure into which varying speeds of wind can be blown so that the action of air against airplanes, rockets, or other objects can be studied. Scale models or full-sized objects may be tested in this manner.

INDEX

(References to illustrations are in italics)

Acceleration, effects of, 100, 102

Acceleration Laboratory, 100

Agena space craft, 169

Allen, H. Julien, 64, *65*

Ames Aeronautical Laboratory, 56

Apollo, Project, 168–70, 173, *174*

Arabian, Don, 157

Armstrong, Neil, 126

Astronauts of Project Mercury, description of, 85–95
  qualifications of, 75–76, 78–79, 82
  tests given to, 79, *80*, 81
  training of, 96–108
  See also specific names of astronauts

Atlantic Missile Range, 3

Atlas intercontinental ballistic missile, 52, 55, 60–61, 63–64, 68, *69*, 70, 118, 141

Friendship 7 boosted by, 146, 148
  size of, 70
  thrust of, 70, 109–10
  varieties of, 70–71

Aurora 7, 164

Ballistic missile, defined, 70

Bland, Bill, 157

Boeing Airplane Company, 130

Bonney, Walter, 96

Cape Canaveral, 3–4, 23, 55, 71, 110, 116, 142, 144–45

Capsule, space, *see* Space capsule

Capsule Communicator, 15

Carbon dioxide, removed from space capsule, 30

Carpenter, Malcolm Scott, *80*, 83, 84, *89*, 142
  description of, 85–86

Project Mercury training of, 96–97, *101*
three-orbit flight of, 164, 167
Centrifuge, Johnsville, 100, *101*, 102–03, 127
Chew, John, *59*
Chimpanzees, in space capsule, 110, *111*, 112, 119–20
Communication satellite, 32
Control Center (Project Mercury), 15, 19–20, 71, 74, *115*, 148, 150–52, 154, 156, 159
Cooper, Leroy Gordon, Jr., *83*, 84, *89*, 153, 155
description of, 86–87
training of, 96–97
Cosmic rays, 24, 47
Countdown, 14
for Freedom 7, 15
for Friendship 7, 145–46, 148
Crossfield, Scott, 126–27, *128*

Deceleration, effects of, 102
Docking method, for reaching moon, 170
Douglas, William, *147, 149*
Drogue, 20, 64
Dyna-Soar glider, 129–31

Edwards Air Force Base, 56, 121, 127
Eisenhower, Dwight D., 54–55
Enos (chimpanzee), 119, 141–42
Escape rocket, 14, 66, 114

Explorer I, 47, 52, 54
Explorer II, 52
Explorer III, 52, *53*

Freedom 7, 10, *12*, 15, 17–20, *21*
Friendship 7, 146, 148, 150–54, *155*, 156–57, *158*, 159–62, 175

Gagarin, Yuri, 6, 132–35, *136*, 137, 140
Galaxies, 24, 26
Galileo, 26–27
Gantry elevator, *11*
Gemini, Project, 169–70, *171*
General Dynamics Astronautics, 70
Gilruth, Robert R., 57, *59*
Glenn, John Herschel, Jr., 6, 10, 13, 30, 77, *83*, 84, *89*, 113
description of, 87–88, 90
Mercury Project training of, 96–97, *99*
orbital space flight of, 141, *143*, 146, *147*, 148, 150, 152, *155*, 157, *158*, 162, *163*, 164, *165*, *166*, 167, 175
delays in, 142, 144–45
observations during, 151, 153–54, 156
and reëntry, 159–60, *161*, 162, *163*
Glennan, T. Keith, 55
Goddard, Robert H., 36, *37*, 38
Goddard Space Flight Center,

56, 150, 152
Goodrich Company, B. F., 9
Gravity, pull of, 102
Grissom, Virgil Ivan, 6, 10, 13, 59, *83*, 84, *89*
  description of, 90–91
  Project Mercury training of, 96–97, *105*
  Redstone flight by, 113–14, *115*, 116, *117*, 118
Guided missile, defined, 70
Guided Missile Development Division, 54
Gunpowder, invented by Chinese, 33

Ham (chimpanzee), 110, *111*, 112
Hangar S, 6–7, 9, 146
Helicopter, for recovering capsule, *21*, 22–23, 116, 167
High Speed Flight Station, 56
Hold, during countdown, 14
Holloman Air Force Base, 119
Huntsville, Alabama, 54, 56

Iconel-X, 122, 126
Intercontinental ballistic missile, Atlas, *see* Atlas
International Geophysical Year, 50
Intrepid, 167
Isolation, effects of, 31

Johnsville centrifuge, 100, *101*, 102–03, 127
Jupiter-C rocket, 52

Kennedy, John F., 132
Key, Francis Scott, 34
Kleinknecht, Kenneth, 157
Kraft, Christopher Columbus, 156–57

Laika (dog), 47, 133
Lake Champlain, 22–23
Langley Field, 96–98
Langley Laboratory, 56–57, 103
Lewis Flight Propulsion Laboratory, 56–57, 103
Liberty Bell 7, 116
Lippershey, Hans, 26
Liquid oxygen, 10
Little Joe rocket, 109, 112
Loki rocket, 49
Lovelace Clinic, 79, 81

McDonnell Aircraft Corporation, 67–68, 169
McElroy, Neil, 52
McKay, Jack, 126
Mare Imbrium, 168
Mars, 56, 137
MASTIF, 103–04, *105*, 109
Mercury, Project, 4, 6, 10, 13, 19, 57–62, 71, 74, 175
  astronauts chosen by, 75–76, 78–79, *80*, 81–82, *83*, 84–95
  astronauts trained by, 96–108
  Control Center of, 15, 19–20, 71, 74, *115*, 148, 150–52, 154, 156, 159
  space capsule of, 60–61, 63–

64, *65*, 66–68, *69*, 71
    for orbital space flight,
        142, 145–46, 148, 150–
        54, *155*, 156–57, *158*,
        159–60, *161*, 162, *163*,
        164, *165*, *166*, 167
    test shots for, 109–20
    tracking stations of, *72*, *73*,
        152–53
Meteors, 24, 28, 47
Micrometeors, 31–32
Miss Sam (monkey), 112
Moffett Naval Air Station, 56
Moon, 56
    future exploration of, 168–
        70
Motion, Newton's laws of, 33–
    34
Multiple Axis Space Test Fa-
    cility (MASTIF), 103–04,
    105, 109
Multiple-stage rocket, 42–43,
    71

National Advisory Committee
    for Aeronautics, 55–56
National Aeronautics and
    Space Administration, 9, 55–
    58, 96, 121, 126, 167, 175
Newton, Isaac, 33–34
Noa, 160, *161*
North American Aviation
    Company, 126
Nova rocket, 170

Oberth, Hermann, 38
"Operation Paperclip," 40
Orbital space flights, Ameri-
can, 148, 150–54, *155*, 156–
    57, *158*, 159–60, *161*, 162,
    163, 164, *165*, *166*, 167
    Soviet, 133–35, 137–40
Orbiter, Project, 49–50, 52
Override button, 19
Oxygen, for space capsule, 28

Parachute, 20, 64, 114
Peenemuende, 39–40
Pioneer IV, *29*
Pressurization, 28, 67
Project Mercury, *see* Mercury,
    Project
Prospector program, 173

Radio telescope, 27, *29*
Randolph, USS, *117*, 118
Ranger program, 170
Redstone Arsenal, 49
Redstone rocket, 10, 13–15, *16*,
    17–18, 49–50, 52, 58, 70, 97,
    109–10, 112 *ff*.
Retro-rocket, 19, 157, 159
Rocket(s), early Chinese, 33–
    34
    first liquid-fueled, 36, *37*
    Jupiter-C, 52
    Little Joe, 109, 112
    Loki, 49
    as military weapon, 34, 38–
        39
    multiple-stage, 42–43, 71
    Nova, 170
    Redstone, 10, 13–15, *16*, 17–
        18, 49–50, 52, 58, 70, 97,
        109–10, 112 *ff*.

Saturn, 170, *172*, 173
sounding, 42, 44
Titan II, 169
V-2, 39–40, *41*, 42
Vanquard, 50, *51*
Viking, 42
WAC Corporal, 42, *45*
Rocket Research and Development Center, 40
Rogallo Wing, *171*
Rushworth, Robert, 126

Sam (monkey), 112
Satellites, artificial earth, 46
American, 52, *53*, 54, 56
information obtained from, 32, 44, 48
Soviet, 46–47, 50, 52, 54, 58, 133
Saturn rocket, 170, *172*, 173
Schirra, Walter Marty, Jr., *80*, *83*, 84, 89, 156, 159
description of, 91–93
training of, 96–97
SCORE, Project, 54
Shepard, Alan Bartlett, Jr., 4, 6–7, 10, 13–14, 17, 19, *89*, 112, *149*, 151, 154, 156–57, 159
chosen and trained by Project Mercury, 96–97
description of, 93–94
Freedom 7 entered by, *12*, 13, *83*, 84
on gantry elevator, *11*
space suit of, 7, *8*, 9
and take-off, 15–17
view through periscope of

capsule, 18–19
water landing by, 20, *21*, 22–23
Simulators, for space flight, 98, 100
Slayton, Donald Kent, *83*, 84, 89, *149*
description of, 94–95
training of, 96–97
Solar system, 24
Sounding rocket, 42, 44
Soviet Union, space program of, 4, 6, 46–47, 61, 132–40
Space, beginning of, 24
benefits from exploration of, 32
radiations in, 27–28, 31, 47–48
temperatures in, 27
Space capsule, 28
air-conditioning for, 30, 67
blunt shape for, 64
carbon dioxide removed from, 30
chimpanzee in, 110, *111*, 112, 119–20, 141
couch in, 66–67
escape hatch of, training to use, 106, *107*
instrument panel of, 67
meteors as danger to, 31
oxygen for, 28
with "picture" window, 113–14
pressurized, 28, 67
of Project Mercury, *see* Mercury, Project, space capsule of

Space Capsule Recovery Task Force, 22
Space medicine, 60
Space suit, 7, *8*, 9
Space Task Group, 57–58, 60–62, 67–68, 71, 73, 75–76, 97
Spacemen, *see* Astronauts
Spaceship(s), Apollo, 170, 173, *174*
  Gemini, 169, *171*
  Soviet, 133–35, 137–40
Sputniks, 46–47, 49–50, 52, 54, 58
Stars, study of, 26
Sun, 24
Surveyor program, 173

Telemeter, 43
Telescope, 27
  invention of, 26
  radio, 27, *29*
Television, world-wide, through communication satellites, 32
Thrust, of Atlas, 70
  required for reaching moon, 169–70
Titan II, 169
Titov, Gherman, *136*, 137–40, 154, 167
Tracking stations, *72*, 73, 152–54

Ultraviolet rays, in space, 31

V-1 "flying bomb," 39
V-2 rocket, 39–40, *41*, 42
Van Allen, James A., *29*, 31
Van Allen radiation belts, 31, 47

Vanguard, Project, 50, 52, 55–56
Vanguard rocket, 50, *51*
Vanguard satellite, 52
Venus, 56, 137
Viking rocket, 42
Von Braun, Magnus, 40
Von Braun, Wernher, 38–40, *41*, 47, 49-50, 52, *53*, 54, 56, 170
Vostok I, 6, 134–35, 137
Vostok II, 138–40

WAC Corporal rocket, 42, *45*
Walker, Joseph, 126, *128*, 129
Wallops Island, 56
Wan-Hoo, 34
War of 1812, rockets used in, 34, *35*
Weather satellites, 32
Weightlessness, 17, 30, 104, 106, 162
Wendover Air Force Base, 122
Wendt, Guenter, 13, *143*
White, Alvin, 126, *128*, 129
White Sands Proving Ground, *41*, 42–44, 47, 54
Williams, Walter C., *59*, 164
World War II, rockets used in, 39
Wright Patterson Air Force Base, 81

X-15 rocket plane, 121–22, *123*, 124, *125*, 126–27, *128*, 129–31
X-rays, in space, 31

Ziolovsky, Kontantin, 34, 36, 140

LANDMARK BOOKS

1 The Voyages of Christopher Columbus
2 The Landing of the Pilgrims
3 Pocahontas and Captain John Smith
4 Paul Revere and the Minute Men
5 Our Independence and the Constitution
6 The California Gold Rush
7 The Pony Express
8 Lee and Grant at Appomattox
9 The Building of the First Transcontinental Railroad
10 The Wright Brothers
11 Prehistoric America
12 The Vikings
13 The Santa Fe Trail
14 The Story of the U.S. Marines
15 The Lewis and Clark Expedition
16 The Monitor and the Merrimac
17 The Explorations of Pere Marquette
18 The Panama Canal
19 The Pirate LaFitte and the Battle of New Orleans
20 Custer's Last Stand
21 Daniel Boone
22 Clipper Ship Days
23 Gettysburg
24 The Louisiana Purchase
25 Wild Bill Hickock Tames the West
26 Betsy Ross and the Flag
27 The Conquest of the North and South Poles
28 Ben Franklin of Old Philadelphia
29 Trappers and Traders of the Far West
30 Mr. Bell Invents the Telephone
31 The Barbary Pirates
32 Sam Houston, the Tallest Texan
33 The Winter at Valley Forge
34 The Erie Canal
35 Thirty Seconds Over Tokyo
36 Thomas Jefferson, Father of Democracy
37 The Coming of the Mormons
38 George Washington Carver
39 John Paul Jones, Fighting Sailor
40 The First Overland Mail
41 Teddy Roosevelt and the Rough Riders

42 To California by Covered Wagon

43 Peter Stuyvesant of Old New York

44 Lincoln and Douglas: The Years of Decision

45 Robert Fulton and the Steamboat

46 The F.B.I.

47 Dolly Madison

48 John James Audubon

49 Hawaii, Gem of the Pacific

50 War Chief of the Seminoles

51 Old Ironsides: The Fighting *Constitution*

52 The Mississippi Bubble

53 Kit Carson and the Wild Frontier

54 Robert E. Lee and the Road of Honor

55 Guadalcanal Diary

56 Commodore Perry and the Opening of Japan

57 Davy Crockett

58 Clara Barton, Founder of The American Red Cross

59 The Story of San Francisco

60 Up the Trail from Texas

61 Abe Lincoln: Log Cabin to White House

62 The Story of D-Day: June 6, 1944

63 Rogers' Rangers and the French and Indian War

64 The World's Greatest Showman: The Life of P. T. Barnum

65 Sequoyah: Leader of the Cherokees

66 Ethan Allen and the Green Mountain Boys

67 Wyatt Earp: U.S. Marshal

68 The Early Days of Automobiles

69 The Witchcraft of Salem Village

70 The West Point Story

71 George Washington: Frontier Colonel

72 The Texas Rangers

73 Buffalo Bill's Great Wild West Show

74 Evangeline and the Acadians

75 The Story of the Secret Service

76 Tippecanoe and Tyler Too!

77 America's First World War: General Pershing and the Yanks

78 The Doctors Who Conquered Yellow Fever

79 Remember the Alamo!

80 Andrew Carnegie and the Age of Steel
81 Geronimo: Wolf of the Warpath
82 The Story of the Paratroops
83 The American Revolution
84 The Story of the Naval Academy
85 Alexander Hamilton and Aaron Burr
86 Stonewall Jackson
87 The Battle for the Atlantic
88 The First Transatlantic Cable
89 The Story of the U.S. Air Force
90 The Swamp Fox of the Revolution
91 Heroines of the Early West
92 The Alaska Gold Rush
93 The Golden Age of Railroads
94 From Pearl Harbor to Okinawa
95 The Copper Kings of Montana
96 Great American Fighter Pilots of World War II
97 The Story of the U.S. Coast Guard
98 William Penn: Quaker Hero
99 John F. Kennedy and PT-109
100 The Story of Oklahoma
101 Americans into Orbit: The Story of Project Mercury
102 The Story of Submarines

WORLD LANDMARK BOOKS

W-1 The First Men in the World
W-2 Alexander the Great
W-3 Adventures and Discoveries of Marco Polo
W-4 Joan of Arc
W-5 King Arthur and His Knights
W-6 Mary, Queen of Scots
W-7 Napoleon and the Battle of Waterloo
W-8 Royal Canadian Mounted Police
W-9 The Man Who Changed China: The Story of Sun Yat-Sen
W-10 The Battle of Britain

W-11 The Crusades

W-12 Genghis Khan and the Mongol Horde

W-13 Queen Elizabeth and the Spanish Armada

W-14 Simon Bolivar, the Great Liberator

W-15 The Slave Who Freed Haiti: The Story of Toussaint Louverture

W-16 The Story of Scotland Yard

W-17 The Life of St. Patrick

W-18 The Exploits of Xenophon

W-19 Captain Cook Explores the South Seas

W-20 Marie Antoinette

W-21 Will Shakespeare and the Globe Theater

W-22 The French Foreign Legion

W-23 Martin Luther

W-24 The Hudson's Bay Company

W-25 Balboa: Swordsman and Conquistador

W-26 The Magna Charta

W-27 Leonardo Da Vinci

W-28 General Brock and Niagara Falls

W-29 Catherine the Great

W-30 The Fall of Constantinople

W-31 Ferdinand Magellan: Master Mariner

W-32 Garibaldi: Father of Modern Italy

W-33 The Story of Albert Schweitzer

W-34 The Marquis de Lafayette: Bright Sword for Freedom

W-35 Famous Pirates of the New World

W-36 Exploring the Himalaya

W-37 Queen Victoria

W-38 The Flight and Adventures of Charles II

W-39 Chief of the Cossacks

W-40 The Adventures of Ulysses

W-41 William the Conqueror

W-42 Jesus of Nazareth

W-43 Julius Caesar

W-44 The Story of Australia

W-45 Captain Cortés Conquers Mexico

W-46 Florence Nightingale

W-47 The Rise and Fall of Adolf Hitler

W-48 The Story of Atomic Energy

W-49 Great Men of Medicine

W-50 Cleopatra of Egypt

W-51 The Sinking of the Bismarck

W-52 Lawrence of Arabia

W-53 The Life of Saint Paul

W-54 The Voyages of Henry Hudson